# Questions and Answers

# PHYSICS

## KEY STAGE 4

**Graham Booth** Chief Examiner
**Bob McDuell** Chief Examiner

SERIES EDITOR: BOB McDUELL

*Letts*
EDUCATIONAL

# Contents

## HOW TO USE THIS BOOK

The aim of the *Questions and Answers* series is to provide you with help to do as well as possible in your exams at GCSE or, in Scotland, at General and Credit levels. This book is based on the idea that an experienced Examiner can give, through examination questions, sample answers and advice, the help students need to secure success and improve their grades.

This *Questions and Answers* series is designed to provide the following.

- **Introductory advice** on the different types of questions and how to answer them to maximise your marks.

- Information about the other skills, apart from the recall of knowledge, that will be tested on examination papers. These are sometimes called **Assessment objectives** and include communication, problem solving, evaluation and interpretation (see pages 5–6). The *Questions and Answers* series is intended to develop these skills by showing you how marks are allocated.

- **Revision summaries** to remind you of the topics you will need to have revised in order to answer examination questions.

- Many examples of **examination questions**, arranged by topic, with spaces for you to fill in your answers, just as on an examination paper. Only try the questions once you have revised a topic thoroughly. Read the Revision summary, before attempting the questions, to double-check you know the topic. It is best not to consult the answers before trying the questions.

- **Sample answers** to all of the questions.

- **Advice from Examiners**. By using the experience of actual Chief Examiners we are able to give advice on how you can improve your answers and avoid the most common mistakes.

This book is designed to help those studying for both double award science and physics. For students of double award science, the material up to the line in the revision summaries and questions should be studied and the rest omitted. **Physics students should study the material up to the line and the material beyond the line that applies to their syllabus.** If in doubt about which material beyond the line applies to you, check with your teacher or the syllabus booklet.

## THE IMPORTANCE OF USING QUESTIONS FOR REVISION

Past examination questions play an important part in revising for examinations. However, it is important not to start practising questions too early. Nothing can be more disheartening than trying to do a question which you do not understand because you have not mastered the topic. Therefore, it is important to have studied a topic thoroughly before attempting any questions on it.

How can past examination questions provide a way of preparing for the examination? It is unlikely that any question you try will appear in exactly the same form on the papers you are going to take. However, the Examiner is restricted on what can be set because the questions must cover the whole syllabus and test certain Assessment objectives. The number of totally original questions that can be set on any part of the syllabus is very limited and so similar ideas occur over and over again. Certainly, it will help you if the question you are trying to answer in an examination is familiar and if you know you have done similar questions before. This is a great boost for your confidence and confidence is what is required for examination success.

Practising examination questions will also highlight gaps in your knowledge and understanding which you can go back and revise more thoroughly. It will also indicate which sorts of questions you can do well and which, if there is a choice of questions, you should avoid.

Attempting past questions will get you used to the type of language used in questions.

Finally, having access to answers, as you do in this book, will enable you to see clearly what is required by the Examiner, how best to answer each question, and the amount of detail required. Attention to detail is a key aspect of achieving success at GCSE.

# EXAMINATION TECHNIQUE

Success in GCSE examinations comes from proper preparation and a positive attitude to the examination. This book is intended to help you overcome 'examination nerves', which often come from a fear of not being properly prepared. Examination technique is extremely important and certainly affects your performance. Remember the basics:

- read the questions carefully;
- make sure that you watch the time carefully and complete the paper; it is no good answering one question well if you spend so long doing it that you do not answer another question at all;
- read the rubric on the front of the examination paper carefully to make sure you know how many questions to attempt;
- examination papers usually tell you how many marks are available for each answer; take notice of this information as the number of marks gives a guide to the importance of the question and often to the amount you ought to write;
- check before the end of the examination that you have not missed any pages and remember to turn over the last page;
- remember to leave time to check through your work carefully.

# DIFFERENT TYPES OF EXAMINATION QUESTION

## Structured questions

These are the most common type of question used at GCSE on physics papers. All of the questions in this book are structured questions. The reason why they are so widely used is that they are so versatile. They can be short with little opportunity for extended writing. In this form, they are suitable for use on Foundation tier papers. Alternatively, they can be longer and more complex in their structure with opportunities for extended writing and demonstration of the higher level skills of interpretation and evaluation. In this form, they are suitable for Higher tier papers.

In a structured question, the question is divided into parts (a), (b), (c), etc. These parts can be further subdivided into (i), (ii), (iii), (iv), etc. A structure is built into the question and hence into your answer. This is where the term 'structured question' comes from.

For each part of the question there are a number of lines or a space for your answer. This is a guide to you about the detail required in the answer, but it does not have to limit you. If you require more space continue your answer on a separate sheet of paper, but make sure you label the answer clearly, e.g. 3(a)(ii).

For each part of the question there is a number in brackets, e.g. (3), to show you how many marks are allocated to this part of the question by the Examiner. If a part is worth three marks, for example, the question requires more than one or two words. As a general rule, if there are three marks allocated, you will need to make three points.

To give you a guide as you work through structured questions, papers are often designed to enable you to score one mark per minute. Therefore, a question worth a maximum of 15 marks should take about 15 minutes to answer.

You do not have to write your answers in full sentences. Concise notes are often the most suitable response. It is very important, if you have time at the end of the examination, to check your answers for accuracy. Read your answers to yourself, not aloud, and check that they make sense.

It is most important to read the stimulus material in the question thoroughly and more than once. This information is often not used fully by students and, as a result, the question is not answered fully. The key to answering many of these questions comes from the appreciation of the full meaning of the 'command word' at the start of the question – 'state, describe, explain'.

The following glossary of command words may help you in the answering of structured questions.

- **State** This means a brief answer is required with no supporting evidence. Alternatives include **write down**, **give**, **list** and **name**.
- **Define** Just a definition is required.
- **State and explain** A short answer is required (see **state**), but then an explanation is required. A question of this type should be worth more than one mark.
- **Describe** This is often used with reference to a particular experiment. The important points should be given about each stage. Again this type of question is worth more than one mark.
- **Outline** The answer should be brief and the main points picked out.
- **Predict** A brief answer is required, without supporting evidence. You are required to make logical links between various pieces of information.
- **Complete** You are required to add information to a diagram, sentence, flow chart, graph, key, table, etc.
- **Find** This is a general term which may mean calculate, measure, determine, etc.
- **Calculate** A numerical answer is required. You should show your working in order to get an answer. Do not forget the correct units.
- **Suggest** There is not just one correct answer or you are applying your answer to a situation outside the syllabus.

## Free response questions

These can include essay questions. In this type of question you are given a question which enables you to develop your answer in different ways. Your answer really is a free response and you write as much as you wish. Candidates often do not write enough or try to 'pad out' the answer. Remember, you can only score marks when your answer matches the marking points on the examiner's marking scheme.

In this type of question it is important to plan your answer before starting it, allocating the correct amount of time to each part of the question.

### Sample question

Choose one part of the electromagnetic spectrum. Describe one use of the waves in that part of the spectrum. Explain how the properties of the waves make them suitable for the use that you have described. (6)

Describe how the waves you have chosen fit into the electromagnetic spectrum. (3)

This question should take about 10–15 minutes to answer. In preparation you need to consider which part of the spectrum to choose. It is a good idea to choose a part of the spectrum that you know something about and can give an example of a use. There is no mark for choosing the waves.

3

*Answer plan:* Choose X-rays and describe their use to examine broken bones. Include absorption or transmission through flesh or bone.

Here is a sample answer.

X-rays can be used to examine parts of the body for bone fractures.

*[1 mark for knowing a use for X-rays]*

The X-ray beam is passed through part of a person's leg, for example, and detected by a photographic film placed behind the leg.
*[It is a good idea to use freehand sketches to help to describe a situation or explain a meaning.*

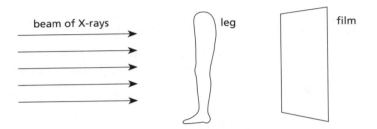

*This helps the Examiner who is marking your paper, because it makes your answer clearer. There are two marks awarded here; one for knowing that X-rays can be detected by photographic film and one for knowing where the film is placed in relation to the leg and the X-ray beam.]*

X-rays are absorbed by bone, but pass easily through flesh.

*[This statement contains two properties of X-rays that make it suitable for the use being described. Each of these properties gains one mark. For the final mark, we need to add the detail of how the fracture is detected.]*

A fracture in the bone shows on the X-ray plate as a dark line because the X-rays have passed through it and affected the plate.

*Now for the second part of the question.*

X-rays are short-wavelength waves.

*[1 mark for knowing where in the spectrum X-rays occur. The question asks how they fit into the spectrum, so for the final two marks two comparisons will be made.]*

They have a longer wavelength than gamma rays and a shorter wavelength than ultra-violet waves.

## Which tier should you enter?

GCSE Physics papers in England and Wales are set in two tiers – Foundation and Higher. There are only certain grades available for each tier. It is important you enter the correct tier.

| Foundation | Higher |
|---|---|
| | A* |
| | A |
| | B |
| C | C |
| D | D |
| E | |
| F | |
| G | |
| U | |

You can be awarded a C or D grade on either tier. If you are aiming at a grade above C you need to take the Higher tier. If you are working at D or even C, you are probably better advised to take the Foundation tier, because if you fail to achieve a grade D on Higher tier you will be ungraded.

Approximately 45% of the marks will be for common questions set on both Higher and Foundation papers. They will be the easy questions on the Higher tier paper and the hard questions on the Foundation tier paper. These questions are used by the Examiners to ensure that grades C and D on the two papers are equivalent. If we assume that each paper contains approximately 20% of the marks for each available grade, a Higher tier paper will have a lot of questions which C grade candidates cannot hope to do, so the mark required for a grade C on Foundation and Higher will be very different.

# ASSESSMENT OBJECTIVES IN PHYSICS

Assessment objectives are the intellectual and practical skills you should be able to show. Opportunities must be made by the Examiner when setting the examination paper for you to demonstrate your mastery of these skills when you answer the question paper.

Traditionally, the Assessment objective of knowledge and understanding has been regarded as the most important skill to develop. Candidates have been directed to learn large bodies of knowledge to recall in the examination. Whilst not wanting in any way to devalue the learning of facts, it should be remembered that on modern papers knowledge and understanding can only contribute about half of the marks available. The other half of the marks are acquired by mastery of the other Assessment objectives, namely to:

- communicate scientific observations, ideas and arguments effectively;
- select and use reference materials and translate data from one form to another;
- interpret, evaluate and make informed judgements from relevant facts, observations and phenomena;
- solve qualitative and quantitative problems.

## 1 Communicate scientific observations, ideas and arguments effectively
(*weighting on papers approximately 5–10%*)

In any examination, communication of information to the examiner is of primary importance. Questions are built into the paper to test your ability to communicate scientific information. Often these questions require extended answers. In this type of question it is important to look at your answer objectively after you have written it and try to judge whether your answer is communicating information effectively.

## 2 Select and use reference materials and translate data from one form to another (*weighting on papers approximately 10–15%*)

| Skill acquired | Approx. grade in GCSE maths |
|---|:---:|
| Read information from graphs or simple diagrams | F |
| Work out simple percentages | F |
| Construct and use pie charts | F |
| Use graphs | E |
| Plot graphs from data provided (the axes and scales are given to you) | E |
| Able to draw lines of best fit through points on a graph | C |
| Select the most appropriate axes and scales for graph plotting | B |

In questions testing this Assessment objective you are often asked to pick information from a chart or table and use it in another form, e.g. to draw a graph, a pie chart or bar chart. You may be asked to complete a table using information from a graph.

It is important to transfer the skills you have acquired in mathematics to your work in physics.

It is reasonable, therefore, to conclude that at Higher tier, you might be required to use a blank piece of graph paper and choose your own scales and axes. Then you would plot the points and draw a line of best fit through the points. If you are doing this, remember the following:

❶ Draw your graph as large as possible on the graph paper by choosing scales appropriately. Avoid choosing scales where, for example, 3 small squares are equivalent to 5°C. It would be better if 1 small square were equivalent to 1°C or 2°C. With this type of graph drawing, marks are usually awarded for the choice of scales and for labelled axes.

❷ Plot each point with a dot or small cross. Circle the dot or cross to make its position clear.

❸ Your line of best fit, whether it is a straight line or a curve, does not have to go through all the points. Some points may not be in the correct place, even if you plotted them correctly, because of inaccuracies in the experiment or experimental error.

On a Foundation tier paper a similar graph may have to be drawn, but it would be more appropriate for the examiner to provide a grid with axes and scales given. Then you would only have to plot the points and draw the line of best fit. It would probably be worth fewer marks than a graph on the Higher tier paper.

### 3 Interpret, evaluate and make informed judgements from relevant facts, observations and phenomena *(weighting on papers approximately 10–15%)*

Questions testing this Assessment objective are often difficult for candidates. It is much easier to test this on a Higher tier paper than on a Foundation tier paper.

The command word 'suggest' is very frequently used as the information given, perhaps in a paragraph, table, diagram or any combination of these, and is open to more than one interpretation.

Look carefully at all of the information given and look for possible alternative interpretations before writing your answer.

### 4 Solve qualitative and quantitative problems *(weighting on papers approximately 10–15%)*

There is no shortage of opportunities to ask questions testing this Assessment objective on physics GCSE papers. Again opportunities are greater, especially for solving quantitative problems, on Higher tier papers.

Qualitative problems can include describing energy transfers or explaining how conservation of energy applies to an energy transfer. Quantitative problems include the full range of physical calculations which have baffled students studying physics for generations. When attempting to carry out a physical calculation, remember to:

❶ use all of the information given to you – if the question gives specific heat capacities, they should be used;

❷ show all of your working, so credit can be given if you do not get the correct answer but do get some way through the question;

❸ take care when substituting in a mathematical formula to be consistent in your units;

❹ give correct units to your answers if there are units and remember that ratios (including efficiencies) do not have units.

You will see questions throughout this book where the question is designed to test Assessment objectives other than knowledge and understanding.

# Formulae that you should know

This is a list of formulae that you may need to use in answering physics questions, but which will not be given to you either on the examination paper or on a separate formula sheet.

**For Foundation tier papers**

power = current × voltage $\qquad\qquad P = I \times V$

voltage = current × resistance $\qquad\quad V = I \times R$

average speed = distance travelled ÷ time taken $\quad v = \dfrac{s}{t}$

acceleration = increase in velocity ÷ time taken $\quad a = \dfrac{(v\text{-}u)}{t}$

pressure = force ÷ area $\qquad\qquad\qquad P = \dfrac{F}{A}$

work done or energy transfer = force × distance moved in its own direction
$$W = F \times d$$

**In addition, for Higher tier papers**

charge = current × time $\qquad\qquad\qquad Q = I \times t$

$\dfrac{\text{primary voltage}}{\text{secondary voltage}} = \dfrac{\text{number of primary turns}}{\text{number of secondary turns}} \quad \dfrac{V_p}{V_s} = \dfrac{N_p}{N_s}$

force = mass × acceleration $\qquad\qquad F = m \times a$

wave speed = frequency × wavelength $\qquad v = f \times \lambda$

Any other formulae that you need will be provided on the examination paper or on a separate formula sheet.

The electron is a fundamental, negatively charged particle that orbits an atomic nucleus. Whenever two objects rub against each other, some electrons are transferred from one to the other. If one of the objects is an insulator, this can lead to a build up of **static charge**. High voltages due to static charge can cause sparks and electric shocks; these are avoided by connecting surfaces to earth. Static charges can be used to clean up the emissions from chimneys; charged smoke particles are **attracted** to a metal plate with the opposite charge and **repelled** from a metal plate with a similar charge.

Movement of charge creates an **electric current**. Electric current is used to transfer energy from the mains supply or a battery to the components in a circuit. The current in a metal is due to movement of electrons; that in a conducting gas or electrolyte is due to the movement of both positively and negatively charged particles.

Current is measured in **amps** (A) using an **ammeter**. In a **series** circuit there is only one current path, so the ammeter gives the same reading wherever it is placed. A **parallel** circuit has two or more current paths. Depending on where the ammeter is placed, it can be used to measure the current in a single path or the total current in two or more paths. Ammeters are always placed in series with other components, so that all the current being measured passes in them. **Voltmeters**, used to measure **voltage**, are always placed in parallel to measure the voltage across a component.

The amount of electric current passing in a circuit depends on the voltage and the **resistance** in the circuit. Increasing the voltage applies a bigger force to the moving charges, giving a faster flow. Resistance is the opposition to the electric current; more resistance in the circuit reduces the current passing.

The formula for calculating resistance is:

$$\text{resistance} = \frac{\text{voltage}}{\text{current}} \qquad \text{or in symbols} \qquad R = \frac{V}{I}$$

Resistance is measured in **ohms** (symbol $\Omega$).

A metal wire whose temperature does not change has a constant resistance. However, the resistance of a lamp filament is much greater when the filament is hot than when it is cold. **Thermistors** have less resistance when warm than when cold and the resistance of a **light dependent resistor** (LDR) depends on its illumination; the brighter the light, the less the resistance.

**Diodes** only allow a current to pass in one direction (shown by an arrow on the circuit symbol). Even then, they only conduct when the voltage rises above a threshold value. Once a diode is conducting, its resistance decreases with increasing current.

Voltage is a measure of the energy transfer in a component or circuit. A 12 V power supply transfers 12 joules of energy to each coulomb of charge. When the charge flows through a lamp, the energy is transferred into heat and light. Voltage measures energy transfer both ways – the voltage across a power supply measures the energy transfer to the charge and the voltage across a component measures the energy transfer **from** the charge.

**Power** measures the energy transferred each second. This is determined by both the current and the voltage.

The following equations show the relationships between current, charge, power and voltage.

$$\text{current (in A)} = \frac{\text{charge flow (in C)}}{\text{time (in s)}} \qquad I = \frac{Q}{t}$$

$$\text{voltage (in V)} = \frac{\text{energy transfer (in J)}}{\text{charge (in C)}} \qquad V = \frac{E}{Q}$$

$$\text{power (in W)} = \text{current (in A)} \times \text{voltage (in V)} \qquad P = IV$$

Electric current from a battery is **direct current** (d.c.), but that from the mains is **alternating current** (a.c.). Charge flow that forms a direct current is always in the same direction, but the flow changes direction in an alternating current.

The domestic electricity supply uses alternating current. Energy is supplied through the live wire, the neutral wire being the return path for the current. The **earth** wire is connected to the ground and is for safety.

Electric appliances need to be fitted with safety features to reduce the risk of fire and electrocution. **Fuses** or **circuit breakers** fitted in the consumer unit should cut off the current if it reaches such a level that the wiring cables are in danger of overheating and igniting. In a similar way, fuses fitted to plugs protect against fire hazard. The fuse wire melts and this stops the current if there is a fault that causes a larger than normal current to pass.

Earth wires should be connected to the casing of any appliance that has a metal case. Should the case become 'live', a large current then passes to earth which melts the fuse and cuts off the electrical supply.

The **joule** is too small a unit for measuring the energy supplied to homes so the electricity supply industry uses the **kilowatt hour**. The energy transferred is calculated using the formula:

$$\text{energy (in kWh)} = \text{power (in kW)} \times \text{time (in h)}$$

**Magnets** have **poles**. These are the strongest parts of the magnet, usually along the faces or at the ends of a bar magnet. Like poles repel each other and unlike poles attract. The **magnetic field** around a magnet is the name given to the region where it exerts forces on magnetic materials; the direction of the field at any point is the direction of the force it exerts on the north-seeking pole of a magnet.

Electric currents also have magnetic fields; a current-carrying wire placed at right angles to the field between two attracting magnets experiences a force that is at right angles to both the current in the wire and the magnetic field direction. This is used in devices such as relays, motors and loudspeakers to produce movement.

**Electromagnetic induction** is the name given to the way in which electricity is generated and transformed. In a generator or bicycle dynamo a magnet rotates inside a coil of wire. The changing magnetic field causes a voltage to be induced; the size of the **induced voltage** depends on the **rate** at which the magnetic field changes.

**Transformers** are efficient devices which use electromagnetism for changing the size of an alternating voltage. The equation for this is:

$$\frac{\text{number of turns on primary coil}}{\text{number of turns on secondary coil}} = \frac{\text{primary voltage}}{\text{secondary voltage}} \qquad \frac{N_p}{N_s} = \frac{V_p}{V_s}$$

Transformers do not give a free supply of energy. When used to increase the voltage they reduce the current and they give increased current when the voltage is reduced.

$$\frac{\text{number of turns on primary coil}}{\text{number of turns on secondary coil}} = \frac{\text{secondary current}}{\text{primary current}} \qquad \frac{N_p}{N_s} = \frac{I_s}{I_p}$$

The electricity supply industry makes extensive use of transformers – transmitting energy at high voltages enables low currents to be used which reduces the energy losses in transmission. Transformers **step up** the voltage at the power station before the energy is fed into the grid and **step down** the voltage in several stages before the energy is delivered to homes, commerce and industry.

---

Adding resistors in series causes the effective resistance to increase. Adding resistors in parallel causes the effective resistance to decrease. The effective resistance of a combination is calculated using:

**series** $\quad R_E = R_1 + R_2 + R_3$ **parallel** $\quad \dfrac{1}{R_E} = \dfrac{1}{R_1} + \dfrac{1}{R_2} + \dfrac{1}{R_3}$

**REVISION
SUMMARY**

Two resistors in series form a **potential divider**, used to divide a voltage supply into two parts.

All electronic systems have an **input**, a **processor** and an **output**. The input is often a potential divider; when one of the resistors is a thermistor or an LDR the voltage across it depends on the environmental conditions. This can be used to switch a **logic gate** or **transistor**. Logic gates are electronically operated switches. With the exception of the NOT gate, most common logic gates have two inputs. The name of the gate describes the conditions of the inputs for the output to be 'on', or at logic 1.

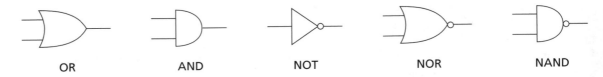

| OR | AND | NOT | NOR | NAND |

Note that **NOR** stands for **NOT OR**; it is the same as an **OR** gate followed by a **NOT**. Similarly, **NAND** acts as an **AND** gate followed by a **NOT**.

A transistor is also an electronically-controlled switch. Current passing from the **collector** to the **emitter** is controlled by the **base**. The transistor is turned on when the base-emitter voltage is 0.7 V or greater, allowing a small current to pass into the base.

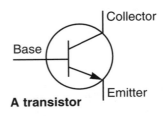

**A transistor**

If you need to revise this subject more thoroughly, see the relevant topics in the *Letts* GCSE *Physics Study Guide* or *CD-ROM*.

The output from a transistor or logic gate can go directly to a **light-emitting diode** to show whether the processor is 'on' or 'off'. To switch output devices such as buzzers, heaters and motors, a **relay** is required. Relays are electromagnetic switches that operate from a low voltage and current and can be used to switch devices that operate from a high voltage and current source.

In a **cathode ray oscilloscope** (CRO), a beam of electrons from an **electron gun** is directed at a fluorescent screen. The beam is made to sweep the screen horizontally at a pre-determined speed by the **time base**. This allows the frequency of an alternating voltage to be measured.

Vertical deflection is achieved by passing the beam between a pair of parallel metal plates with a high voltage between them. The size of an alternating voltage can be measured by the amount of vertical deflection if the vertical (y) sensitivity of the CRO is known.

**1** When plants are sprayed with insecticide the spray droplets are given a positive charge by a spray gun.

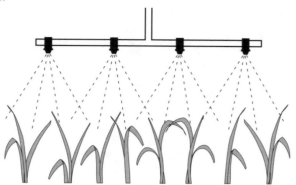

(a) To give the drops a positive charge, does the spray gun add electrons or take electrons away from the drops?

.................................................................................................... (1)

(b) Explain why the drops do not stay together after leaving the gun.

....................................................................................................

.................................................................................................... (2)

(c) Small amounts of electric charge can move about in the plants. What type of charge will be attracted to the surface of the leaves by the positively charged drops?

.................................................................................................... (1)

(d) It is possible to spray the plants with droplets which are not charged. Describe and explain one advantage of using charged drops.

....................................................................................................

.................................................................................................... (2)

*Edexcel 1991*

**2** (a) Write down the ammeter readings A1 to A4.

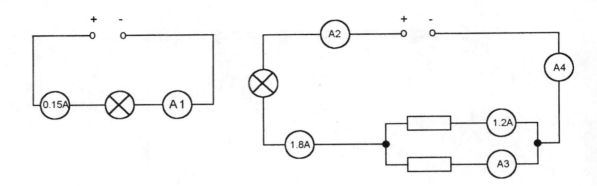

A1 reads ...................................

A2 reads ...................................

A3 reads ...................................

A4 reads ...................................                    (4)

(b) Write down the readings on voltmeters V1 and V2.

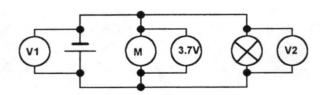

V1 reads ...................................

V2 reads ...................................                    (2)

**3** A student compares three different metal wires to see which is the best conductor of electricity. He passes a current of 0.8 A in each wire in turn and measures the voltage needed. The table shows his results.

| Wire | Voltage/V |
|------|-----------|
| A | 5.2 |
| B | 0.6 |
| C | 12.4 |

(a) Which wire is the best conductor of electricity? Explain your choice.

.................................................................................................................................

................................................................................................................... (2)

(b) Calculate the resistance of wire B.

.................................................................................................................................

.................................................................................................................................

................................................................................................................... (3)

(c) While doing the experiment, the student notices that one of the wires gets hot. Calculate the power in each wire and use your answers to explain which wire gets hot.

.................................................................................................................................

.................................................................................................................................

.................................................................................................................................

.................................................................................................................................

................................................................................................................... (5)

(d) Calculate the quantity of electric charge that passes through each wire in one minute.

.................................................................................................................................

.................................................................................................................................

................................................................................................................... (3)

4 The diagram shows part of the lighting circuit in a house.

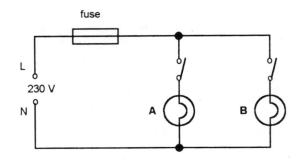

(a) Lamp A is a 60 W lamp.

Calculate the current in the lamp when it is switched on.

..........................................................................................................................................................

..........................................................................................................................................................

.......................................................................................................................................... (3)

(b) When both switches are closed, the current in the fuse is measured to be 0.76 A.

Calculate the resistance of lamp B.

..........................................................................................................................................................

..........................................................................................................................................................

..........................................................................................................................................................

.......................................................................................................................................... (4)

(c) Explain how the fuse can act as a safety device in this circuit.

..........................................................................................................................................................

..........................................................................................................................................................

.......................................................................................................................................... (3)

*MEG 1996*

5   The diagram below shows a door lock which can be opened from a flat inside a building.

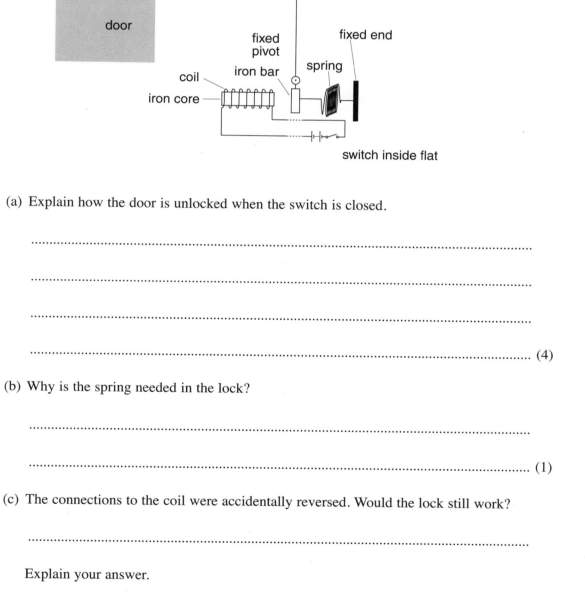

(a) Explain how the door is unlocked when the switch is closed.

..............................................................................................................

..............................................................................................................

..............................................................................................................

.............................................................................................. (4)

(b) Why is the spring needed in the lock?

..............................................................................................................

.............................................................................................. (1)

(c) The connections to the coil were accidentally reversed. Would the lock still work?

..............................................................................................................

Explain your answer.

..............................................................................................................

..............................................................................................................

.............................................................................................. (2)

*NEAB 1998*

**6** The diagram shows a magnet and a coil of wire which is connected to a sensitive ammeter. When the magnet is moved slowly into the coil, the needle on the ammeter shows a steady deflection to the right.

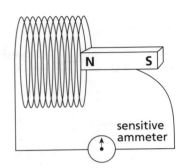

sensitive
ammeter

(a) Explain why there is a reading on the ammeter when the magnet is moved into the coil.

.................................................................................................................................................

.................................................................................................................... (2)

(b) Describe and explain the ammeter reading when the magnet is:

(i) held steady inside the coil.

.................................................................................................................................................

.................................................................................................................... (2)

(ii) withdrawn slowly from the coil.

.................................................................................................................................................

.................................................................................................................... (2)

(iii) moved quickly in and out of the coil.

.................................................................................................................................................

.................................................................................................................... (2)

**7**  A power station produces electricity at 25 000 volts. This voltage is stepped up to 400 000 volts by a transformer.

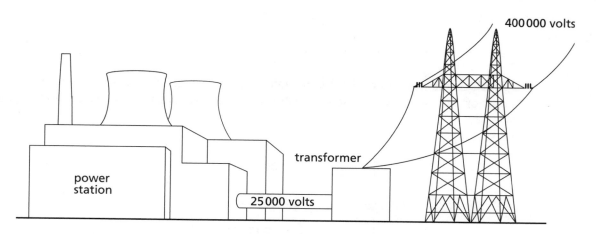

(a)  The number of turns on the primary coil of the transformer is 20 000. Calculate the number of turns on the secondary coil.

...........................................................................................................................

.................................................................................................................... (2)

(b)  Why is a voltage as high as 400 000 volts used in the transmission of electrical energy?

.................................................................................................................... (1)

*SEG 1994*

**8**  The diagram represents an electronic system which is used to control the temperature in an incubator.

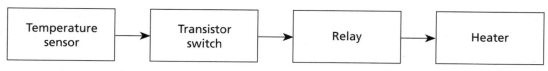

(a)  Identify the input sensor, the processor and the output device in this system.

...........................................................................................................................

...........................................................................................................................

.................................................................................................................... (3)

(b) Explain the purpose of the relay between the transistor switch and the heater.

......................................................................................................................

.................................................................................................................. (2)

The circuit diagram shows how the temperature sensor is made from a fixed resistor and a thermistor. The resistance of the thermistor decreases when its temperature increases.

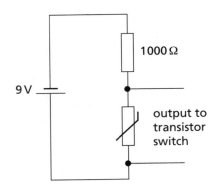

(c) The transistor switch is switched on when the input to it is 0.6 V or more.

(i)   Calculate the voltage across the 1000 Ω resistor when the potential difference across the thermistor is 0.6 V.

.................................................................................................................. (1)

(ii)  Use your value from (i) to calculate the current in the circuit and the resistance of the thermistor when the voltage across the thermistor is 0.6 V.

......................................................................................................................

......................................................................................................................

......................................................................................................................

.................................................................................................................. (4)

(iii) Suggest why the current in the temperature-sensing circuit needs to be low.

......................................................................................................................

.................................................................................................................. (2)

(d) Explain why the transistor switch turns the heater off when the temperature of the thermistor rises.

........................................................................................................

........................................................................................................

........................................................................................... (3)

**9** A burglar alarm is operated by three switches. Switches A and B are fitted to two separate doors and switch M is the master switch. When a door is opened or the master switch is turned on, it causes the input to a logic gate to be 'on'. The diagram shows the circuit which is used.

M ────────────────────┐
                       │
A ──────────┐          │
            │ OR )──── ( AND )──── [ relay ]──── output
B ──────────┘                                    to alarm

(a) Complete the table using a 0 for 'off' and a 1 for 'on'.

|  | Inputs to OR gate | | Inputs to AND gate | | |
|---|---|---|---|---|---|
|  | **A** | **B** | **OR gate output** | **M** | **AND gate output** |
| (i) | 0 | 0 | | 1 | |
| (ii) | 1 | 0 | | 1 | |
| (iii) | 0 | 1 | | 0 | |
| (iv) | 1 | 1 | | 0 | |

(4)

(b) Which line of the table shows what happens when the master switch is 'on' and the doors are closed?

........................................................................................... (1)

(c) Which lines of the table show what happens when a door is opened while the master switch is 'off'?

........................................................................................... (1)

(d) Describe what has to happen for the alarm to sound.

..............................................................................................................................

.................................................................................................................. (2)

(e) Explain the purpose of the relay.

..............................................................................................................................

.................................................................................................................. (2)

Forces can cause objects to change in size or shape, speed or direction of motion. Whenever one object pulls or pushes another, each object exerts the same size force on the other, but the forces are in opposite directions.

Springs and metal wires follow **Hooke's law** when subjected to a stretching force; the extension is proportional to the force up to the limit of proportionality. Materials that return to their original size and shape when a force is removed are said to be elastic. Rubber is elastic, as are metals up to their elastic limit; beyond this they deform permanently. Plasticine and Blu-tack are plastic materials – their shape is easily changed and they retain the new shape when the force is removed.

The **pressure** caused by a force is a measure of how effective it is at piercing or deforming the surface that it acts on. Drawing pins and scissors are designed so that the force exerts a large pressure and penetrates the surface. Skis and caterpillar tracks on vehicles ensure that the force is applied over a large area to reduce the pressure. The formula for calculating pressure is:

$$\text{pressure} = \frac{\text{force}}{\text{area}} \qquad \text{or in symbols} \qquad P = \frac{F}{A}$$

The unit of pressure is the **pascal (Pa)** which is equivalent to a $N/m^2$.

In **hydraulic** systems, liquids are used to transmit pressure. Because liquids exert an equal pressure in all directions, the pressure can be easily transmitted round corners. By changing the **area** over which the pressure acts, the **force** can be made bigger or smaller.

Taps, bicycle pedals and doors are common examples of situations where forces are used to turn things round. How effective a force is at causing rotation depends not only on the size of the force, but also the shortest distance from the line it acts along to the pivot. The **moment**, or **turning effect**, of a force is calculated using the formula:

$$\text{moment} = \text{force} \times \text{shortest (or perpendicular) distance from force line to pivot}$$

The moment, or turning effect, of a force is measured in **Nm**. In situations where the turning effects of a number of forces cancel out, the object is **balanced** or **in equilibrium**. This is known as the '**law of moments**' which states that when an object is in equilibrium, the sum of the clockwise moments about any pivot is equal to the sum of the anticlockwise moments about that pivot.

Cars, bikes, buses, trains and other moving objects often have more than one force acting, so the overall effect of all the forces acting has to be taken into account. If the forces acting cancel out there is no effect on the movement of the object; it either stays put or moves in a straight line at a constant speed.

The **average speed** of a moving object is calculated using the equation:

$$\text{average speed} = \frac{\text{distance travelled}}{\text{time taken}} \qquad \text{or in symbols} \qquad v = \frac{s}{t}$$

Speed can also be calculated from a graph of distance travelled against time. The gradient or slope of the graph represents the speed.

Objects moving with the same speed in different directions have different **velocities**. The velocity of an object gives two pieces of information – its speed and direction.

When the forces are not balanced, the effect is to change the speed or direction of an object. This is known as acceleration, which is calculated using the formula:

$$\text{acceleration} = \frac{\text{increase in velocity}}{\text{time taken}} \qquad \text{or in symbols} \qquad a = \frac{(v - u)}{t}$$

Acceleration can be thought of as the increase in speed per second and is measured in $m/s^2$.

The acceleration caused by an unbalanced force depends on the mass being accelerated as well as the size of the unbalanced force – a double-decker bus needs a much bigger force than a

**REVISION SUMMARY**

mini car to give it the same acceleration. The equation which relates the mass of the object to the size of the unbalanced force and the acceleration it causes is:

$$\text{force} = \text{mass} \times \text{acceleration} \quad \text{or in symbols} \quad F = ma$$

An object falling freely in the absence of air resistance has an acceleration, g, equal to $10\,\text{m/s}^2$. As an object falling through air or any other fluid speeds up, the resistive force increases. The effect of this is to reduce the size of the unbalanced force and the acceleration. Eventually **terminal velocity** is reached when the downward force, the object's **weight**, is balanced by the resistive force.

The **stopping distance** of a vehicle is the distance it travels between the time when a driver notices a hazard and the vehicle coming to rest. The factors that affect stopping distance include the driver's **reaction time**, the speed and mass of the vehicle, and the conditions of the road, tyres and brakes.

Moving objects also have **momentum**. Momentum is a useful concept when predicting the outcome of a collision or the effect that a force has on changing an object's motion. The momentum of an object is calculated using the formula:

$$\text{momentum} = \text{mass} \times \text{velocity} \quad \text{or in symbols} \quad p = mv$$

Momentum is measured in **N s** or **kg m/s**; the units are equivalent. The relationship between force and momentum is:

$$\text{change in momentum} = \text{force} \times \text{time} \quad \text{or in symbols} \quad \Delta p = Ft$$

There are two important factors to remember about momentum. The first is that the total amount of momentum of any system or group of objects stays the same. The second is that when adding the momentum of one object to that of another, the direction has to be taken into account. The diagram illustrates this.

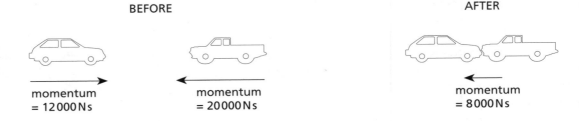

BEFORE

momentum
= 12 000 N s

momentum
= 20 000 N s

AFTER

momentum
= 8 000 N s

If you need to revise this subject more thoroughly, see the relevant topics in the *Letts* GCSE *Physics Study Guide* or CD-ROM.

The **equations of motion** apply to any object moving with a constant acceleration. Each equation is a relationship between four quantities, so if any three are known then the equations can be used to find the unknown quantities. The equations are:

$$v = u + at \qquad v^2 = u^2 + 2as \qquad s = ut + \tfrac{1}{2}at^2 \qquad s = \tfrac{1}{2}(u+v)t$$

where $u$ represents initial velocity and $v$ represents final velocity.

1   The arrows on the diagrams represent the horizontal forces acting on a car which is moving forwards. In each case, the length of the arrow indicates the size of the force.

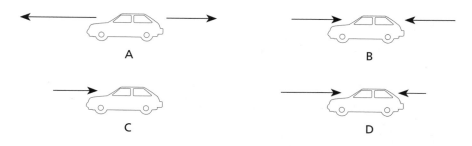

(a) Which diagram or diagrams could represent:

   (i)  a car that is accelerating? ........................................................................................

   (ii) a car that is slowing down? ........................................................................................

   (iii) a car travelling at a constant speed? ............................................................... (4)

(b) (i)  Calculate the average speed of a car that travels 240 m in 16 s.

       ........................................................................................................................

       ........................................................................................................................

       .................................................................................................................. (3)

   (ii) Calculate the time it would take the car to travel at that average speed from Bristol to Hull, a distance of 330 km.

       ........................................................................................................................

       ........................................................................................................................

       .................................................................................................................. (3)

2 The graph shows how the speed of a parachutist changes after jumping from an aircraft.

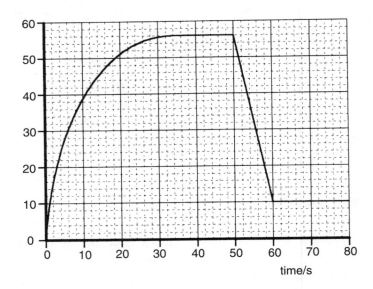

(a) During the first 34 seconds shown on the graph, the velocity of the parachutist is increasing. Describe what is happening to the acceleration of the parachutist and explain why this is happening.

..............................................................................................................................................

..............................................................................................................................................

.................................................................................................................................. (3)

(b) After 50 seconds, the parachute opens. Calculate the acceleration of the parachutist during the next 10 seconds.

..............................................................................................................................................

..............................................................................................................................................

.................................................................................................................................. (3)

(c) Calculate the distance travelled by the parachutist during the period 60 to 80 seconds shown on the graph.

..............................................................................................................................................

..............................................................................................................................................

.................................................................................................................................. (3)

**3** The diagram shows Jo using a hydraulic lift to raise her car. As she pumps oil into the cylinder, the piston moves up with the car.

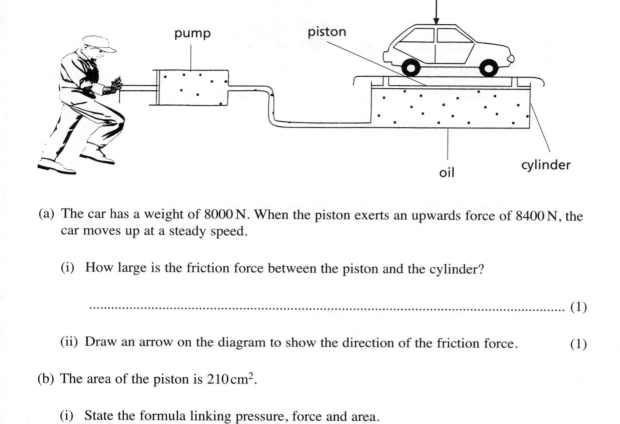

(a) The car has a weight of 8000 N. When the piston exerts an upwards force of 8400 N, the car moves up at a steady speed.

  (i) How large is the friction force between the piston and the cylinder?

  ..................................................................................................... (1)

  (ii) Draw an arrow on the diagram to show the direction of the friction force.  (1)

(b) The area of the piston is 210 cm². 

  (i) State the formula linking pressure, force and area.

  ..................................................................................................... (1)

  (ii) Calculate the oil pressure needed to raise the car at a steady speed.

  .....................................................................................................

  .....................................................................................................

    oil pressure needed = ......................................... N/cm²    (2)

(c) Jo cannot raise the car without the hydraulic lift.
Explain how the lift helps.

  .....................................................................................................

  ..................................................................................................... (2)

*MEG 1995*

**4** The Highway Code gives tables of the shortest stopping distances for cars travelling at various speeds. An extract from the Highway Code is given below.

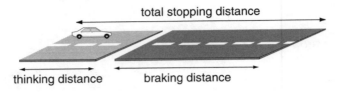

thinking distance + braking distance = total stopping distance

(a) A driver's reaction time is 0.7 s.

    (i) Write down **two** factors which could increase a driver's reaction time.

       1 ................................................................................................................................

       2 ............................................................................................................................ (2)

    (ii) What effect does an increase in reaction time have on:

       A  thinking distance; ........................................................................................

       B  braking distance; ........................................................................................

       C  total stopping distance? ........................................................................ (3)

(b) Explain why the braking distance would change on a wet road.

................................................................................................................................

................................................................................................................................

................................................................................................................................

................................................................................................................................

............................................................................................................................ (2)

(c) A car was travelling at 30 m/s. The driver braked. The graph below is a velocity-time graph showing the velocity of the car during braking.

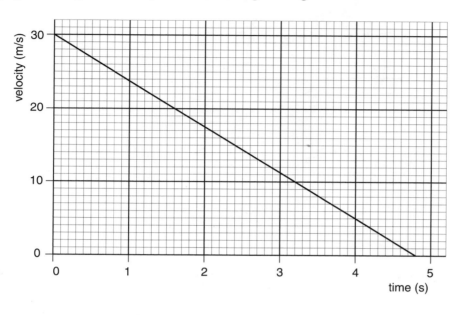

Calculate:

(i) the rate at which the velocity decreases (deceleration);

.................................................................................................

.................................................................................................

Rate ............................ m/s² (2)

(ii) the braking force, if the mass of the car is 900 kg;

.................................................................................................

.................................................................................................

Braking force .................... N (2)

(iii) the braking distance.

.................................................................................................

.................................................................................................

Braking distance ............... m (2)

*NEAB 1998*

**5** A pedestrian steps into the path of an oncoming car. The graph shows how the speed of the car changes from the moment when the driver sees the pedestrian until the car stops.

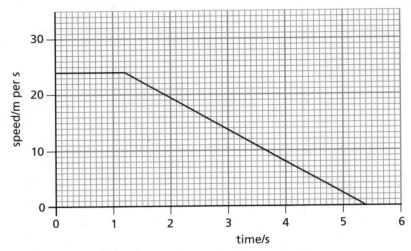

(a) (i) Explain why the first part of the graph shows the car continuing at constant speed.

.............................................................................................................................

......................................................................................................................... (2)

(ii) How far does the car travel in the 1.2 s between the driver seeing the pedestrian and applying the brakes?

.............................................................................................................................

.............................................................................................................................

......................................................................................................................... (3)

(iii) After 1.2 s, the car slows down. Calculate the value of the deceleration of the car in this time.

.............................................................................................................................

.............................................................................................................................

......................................................................................................................... (3)

(iv) Calculate the force which would be needed to cause a driver of mass 85 kg to have the same deceleration.

.............................................................................................................................

.............................................................................................................................

......................................................................................................................... (3)

(b) The sequence of diagrams shows what can happen to the occupants of a car during a collision.

After the car has stopped, the driver continues to move forwards as the seat belt stretches.

(i) Explain why this stretching of the seat belt reduces the force which is exerted on the driver.

.................................................................................................................

.................................................................................................................

................................................................................................... (3)

(ii) Explain why the child who was standing in the back of the car appears to have been thrown forwards.

.................................................................................................................

.................................................................................................................

................................................................................................... (3)

(iii) Modern cars are designed to crumple when they are involved in a collision. Explain how this crumpling of the car helps to protect the occupants from serious injury.

.................................................................................................................

.................................................................................................................

................................................................................................... (3)

*MEG 1991*

6  The diagram shows a simple type of corkscrew.

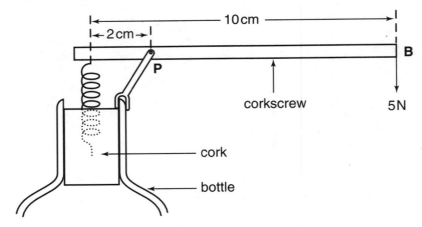

A 5N force applied at **B** is needed to overcome the resistance and pull the cork from the bottle.

(a)  (i) Write down, **in words**, the equation for finding the moment or turning effect of a force about a point.

...................................................................................................................... (1)

(ii) Calculate the moment of the 5 N force about **P**.

...................................................................................................................... (1)

(iii) Calculate the force this produces on the cork.

......................................................................................................................

...................................................................................................................... (2)

(b)  State **one** way in which the design of the corkscrew could be altered so that a smaller force could be used at **B** to pull the cork from the bottle.

...................................................................................................................... (1)

*WJEC 1997*

**7** (a) Calculate the momentum of:

    (i)  a 10 000 kg bus travelling at 15 m/s.

    ..............................................................................................................

    .......................................................................................................... (2)

    (ii) a 100 g bullet travelling at 400 m/s.

    .......................................................................................................... (1)

    (iii) a 500 000 kg jumbo jet cruising at 300 m/s.

    .......................................................................................................... (1)

(b) In foggy conditions on a motorway, vehicles travelling in the same direction can collide.

    ← 15 m/s      ← 25 m/s

    (i)  Calculate the momentum of a 30 000 kg lorry travelling at 25 m/s and that of a 20 000 kg lorry travelling at 15 m/s.

    ..............................................................................................................

    ..............................................................................................................

    ..............................................................................................................

    .......................................................................................................... (4)

    (ii) The heavier lorry collides with the back of the lighter one and they stick together. Calculate the common speed immediately after the collision.

    ..............................................................................................................

    ..............................................................................................................

    ..............................................................................................................

    .......................................................................................................... (4)

# 3 Waves

Waves transfer energy; they are important for communications as well as heating and lighting the space in which we live.

**Sound** is carried to our ears by a to-and-fro movement of air particles. This to-and-fro movement starts with a **vibrating** object, such as a loudspeaker, which sets the air particles into a **longitudinal** wave motion where the vibrations are along the direction in which the wave is travelling.

The maximum amount of displacement (movement to one side or the other) of the air particles is called the **amplitude** of the wave. The greater the amplitude, the louder the sound. The graph shows how the movement of an individual air particle changes with time.

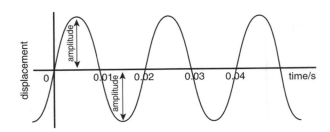

As well as showing the amplitude, the graph has a time scale that enables the **frequency** to be measured. The frequency of a wave is the number of oscillations per second. The sound wave shown on the graph does one complete oscillation in 0.02 s or 1/50 s, so it has a frequency of 50 waves per second, or 50 hertz (Hz). The frequency of a sound wave determines its pitch – 50 Hz is quite a low-pitched sound, but frequencies of 1000 Hz or more are high-pitched.

Measurements of the **wavelength** and **frequency** allow the **speed** of sound to be calculated using the formula:

$$\text{speed} = \text{frequency} \times \text{wavelength} \quad \text{or in symbols} \quad v = f\lambda$$

**Reflections** of sound or **ultrasound**, a longitudinal wave with a frequency above the range of human hearing, are called echoes. Echoes can be used to measure distances and to scan body organs.

**Light** is a small part of a family of waves called the **electromagnetic spectrum**. Most objects do not give off light, so we rely on reflected light to be able to see them. All but the smoothest of surfaces reflect light in all directions. Mirrors are smooth surfaces that reflect light in a predictable way – the angles of incidence and reflection are equal. The reflection of light by a mirror causes a **virtual image** to be formed. Our eye–brain system assumes that light travels in straight lines, so when we look into a mirror the reflected light seems to have come from a point the same distance behind the mirror as the object is in front of it.

Mirrors are not the only things that cause the direction in which light travels to change. Light can also change direction when it passes through transparent objects such as glass. The change in speed when light passes from one substance to another is called **refraction**. This causes a change in wavelength and, except when light hits the boundary at a right angle, a change in direction. Although the wavelength and speed both change when light is refracted, the frequency, which determines the colour of the light, remains constant.

Light does not always pass into the new substance when it meets a boundary. Light travelling from glass to air is **totally internally reflected** for angles of incidence greater than 42°. Total internal reflection is used in bicycle reflectors, prism binoculars, cats' eyes and fibre optics.

The table shows the main parts of the electromagnetic spectrum and their uses.

| Wave | Gamma rays | X-rays | Ultra-violet | Visible light | Infra-red | Microwaves | Radio waves |
|------|-----------|--------|--------------|---------------|-----------|------------|-------------|
| Typical wavelength /m | $1 \times 10^{-12}$ | $1 \times 10^{-9}$ | $1 \times 10^{-7}$ | $5 \times 10^{-7}$ | $1 \times 10^{-6}$ | $1 \times 10^{-1}$ | 100 |
| Use | sterilising medical equipment<br><br>treating cancers and tumours<br><br>taking images of body organs | X-ray photographs<br><br>treating cancers and tumours<br><br>taking images of body organs | treatment of skin disorders, responsible for suntans | seeing and transmitting data | heating and armchair operation of TV equipment | cooking and transmitting data | broadcasting |

The shorter wavelength waves are the most penetrative and also the most ionising, so they pose the greatest dangers. Exposure to waves of shorter wavelength than light should be limited.

All electromagnetic waves are **transverse** waves – the vibrations are at right angles to the direction of travel.

All waves spread out when they pass through a narrow opening – this is called **diffraction**. The amount of spreading depends on the size of the opening relative to the wavelength; if the opening is hundreds of wavelengths wide, very little spreading occurs. Maximum spreading occurs when the opening is equal to the wavelength. Sound waves (a typical wavelength of 1 m) spread out when passing through a doorway, but light waves do not.

Both transverse and longitudinal waves pass through the Earth following an earthquake, when layers of rock slip past each other. Longitudinal waves can be detected at all points on the Earth's surface, but transverse waves cannot be detected on the side of the Earth opposite to the disturbance. This provides evidence that the outer core is liquid, as most liquids transmit longitudinal waves but do not transmit tranverse waves.

---

When two or more waves cross at any point, they **interfere** with each other. When waves interfere, they can combine to give an increase or decrease in disturbance at that point. If two wave crests or two wave troughs combine, then constructive interference takes place. However, a wave crest and a trough combine to interfere destructively. Interference can be seen in surface water waves using a ripple tank – two dippers vibrating in step produce lines of constructive and destructive interference.

The separation of the lines of interference increases with increasing wavelength and distance from the sources, but decreases when the sources are placed further apart. The interference of sound waves can be heard if two loudspeakers driven from the same signal generator are used as wave sources. Interference of light waves is more difficult to arrange using two sources. It can be observed by ruling two narrow slits on a blackened microscope slide and illuminating them with a lamp whose filament is parallel to the slits. Bright and light coloured bands can be seen on a screen placed several metres from the microscope slide.

If you need to revise this subject more thoroughly, see the relevant topics in the *Letts* GCSE *Physics Study Guide* or *CD-ROM*.

1  The diagram represents a loudspeaker cone. The dot represents an air particle.

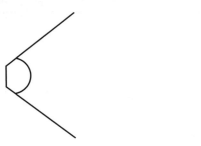

   (a) (i)  Describe the movement of the loudspeaker cone when the loudspeaker is producing
            sound of frequency 200 Hz.

            ...............................................................................................................................................

            ........................................................................................................................ (2)

       (ii)  Draw a series of sketch diagrams to show the movement of the air particle as the
             sound wave passes.




                                                                                                            (4)


   (b)  The graph shows how the displacement of the air particle changes during one cycle of
        the wave.

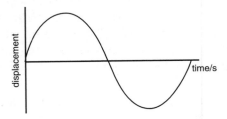

       (i)  Use the axes below to sketch a graph which shows the displacement of the air particle
            when the volume of the sound is reduced with the frequency unaltered.

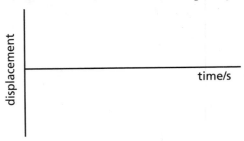

                                                                                                            (2)

(ii) Use the axes below to sketch a graph which shows the displacement of the air molecule with the volume at its original level when the frequency is increased to 400 Hz.

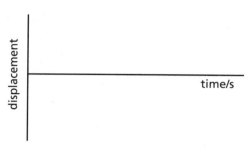

(2)

(c) Sound waves travel in air with a speed of 330 m/s. Calculate the wavelength of a sound wave which has a frequency of 200 Hz.

.............................................................................................................................

.............................................................................................................................

............................................................................................................ (3)

**2** (a) When light passes through a window, it slows down as it enters the glass and speeds up again when it leaves. The speed of light in glass is about two-thirds of the speed of light in air. The diagrams show light waves about to travel through the glass. Complete the diagrams to show the passage of the light through the glass and out at the other side.

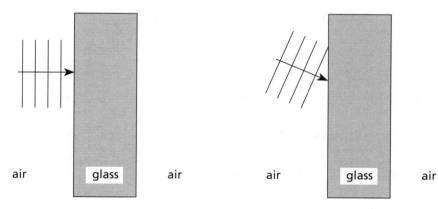

(5)

(b) Periscopes use either mirrors or prisms to turn light round corners. Complete the diagram of a periscope by continuing the light rays until they enter the eye.

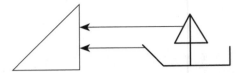

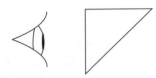

(4)

**3** The diagram shows a transverse wave travelling along a rope.

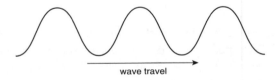

wave travel

(a) Describe the movement of each part of the rope as the wave travels along it.

............................................................................................................................................

............................................................................................................ (2)

(b) Mark with an 'a' a distance which is equal to the amplitude of the wave. (1)

(c) Mark with a 'λ' a distance which is equal to one wavelength of the wave. (1)

(d) When the frequency of the wave is 1.5 Hz, it has a wavelength of 7.5 m.
Calculate the speed of the wave along the rope.

............................................................................................................................................

............................................................................................................................................

............................................................................................................ (3)

4  Both diagrams below show water waves **approaching** the sea shore.

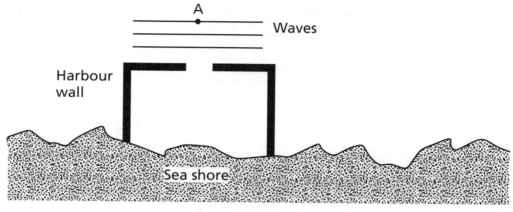

Figure 1

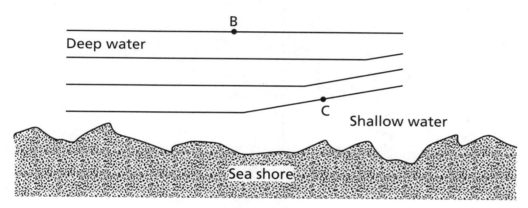

Figure 2

(a)  On the figures, mark carefully the direction of the waves at the points A, B and C.    (3)

(b)  Complete Figure 1 by drawing the waves inside the harbour.
      What name is given to this effect?

      ............................................................................................................ (3)

(c)  What name is given to the change in direction of the waves shown in Figure 2?

      ............................................................................................................ (1)

(d)  State a possible cause of this change of direction.

      ............................................................................................................

      ............................................................................................................ (2)

*NICCEA 1995*

5 Information about two of the types of seismic waves produced by an earthquake is given in the table and diagram.

| Type of wave | Passes through |
|---|---|
| P | solids and liquids |
| S | solids only |

The diagram shows the way that the **P** and **S** waves travel through the Earth from the focus of an earthquake.

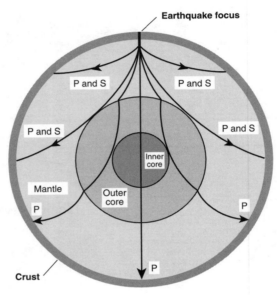

(a) Explain what this information tells us about the structure of the outer core.

............................................................................................................................................

.................................................................................................................... (2)

(b) Explain why this information cannot tell us about the structure of the inner core.

............................................................................................................................................

.................................................................................................................... (2)

(c) As the **P** waves pass from the mantle to the outer core, they change direction. Why?

............................................................................................................................................

.................................................................................................................... (1)

*SEG 1997*

**6** The diagram shows two radio transmitters. The transmitters are broadcasting identical radio waves of wavelength 3.0 m.

A person walks between the transmitters, listening to the broadcast on a Walkman. He notices that the sound gets louder, then quieter, then louder and so on as he walks. When he stands still, the loudness of the sound stays the same, but there are some places where the sound is loud and other places where it is quiet.

(a) Use diagrams to explain how the radio waves from the transmitters combine to give a very strong radio signal at some points and a weak signal at others.

(4)

(b) Suggest why this could be a nuisance to a householder who lives within the range of both transmitters.

..................................................................................................................

.......................................................................................................... (2)

The **Universe** is everything that exists. It is thought to have begun in an enormous explosion about fifteen billion years ago. Within the Universe there are groups of stars called **galaxies**. Our star is the Sun and our galaxy is the **Milky Way**, which is a whirling spiral, held together by the attractive **gravitational forces** that act between massive objects.

Gravitational forces act between all objects that have mass, with each object pulling the other. The size of the gravitational force between two 1 kg masses such as two bags of sugar is tiny, but the size becomes appreciable when one of the objects is massive.

The planets move around the Sun in elliptical orbits that are almost circular. They are kept in orbit by the Sun's gravitational pull. Similarly, the orbit of a planetary moon is due to the planet's gravitational pull on that moon.

Although the Earth has only one natural satellite, there are many artificial ones. Like the Moon, they are kept in orbit by the gravitational attraction of the Earth. This gravitational attraction decreases with increasing distance from the Earth.

Stars are formed in large clouds of gas and dust that contract due to gravitational attraction. As they contract, they heat until the temperature is hot enough for them to generate energy by **nuclear fusion**. After its **main sequence**, a star cools and expands to a **red supergiant**. Contraction due to gravitational forces causes heating. A small star, such as our Sun, becomes a white dwarf and continues to cool, but a large star forms a **blue supergiant**. Further expansion and contraction lead to the formation of a very bright star called a **supernova** which eventually explodes, forming a very dense **neutron star** and a dust cloud. Our Solar System is thought to have formed from the remnants of an exploding supernova.

The core of the dust cloud formed the Sun, with the outermost material condensing to form the planets. In addition to the nine planets, there is the **asteroid belt** and collections of ice and dust known as **comets**. Comets can have very long orbit times, often hundreds of years.

The inner planets, Mercury, Venus, Earth and Mars, are the denser ones in the Solar System – they have a high concentration of metals. Beyond the asteroid belt, Jupiter and Saturn are composed largely of hydrogen and helium. Little is known about the composition of the three outermost planets. Uranus and Neptune are thought to have a rocky core surrounded by a liquid mantle and an atmosphere of hydrogen and helium. Pluto is also thought to be rocky, with a surface of frozen methane.

The Universe is still expanding, as it has been doing since its formation. The rate of expansion is measured from **red shift**, the shifting of the wavelength of the light emitted by a star towards the red end of the spectrum. When the paths of the galaxies are plotted, all these paths trace back to the same point. This is thought to be the point where the Universe was created. The age of the Universe is estimated by measuring the speed at which the galaxies are moving away from each other and extrapolating back to the beginning of time.

There are three possibilities for the future of the Universe. It may carry on expanding forever or the gravitational forces may slow down the expansion and eventually cause it to contract again, with catastrophic results. The third model is that the gravitational forces are not strong enough to cause a collapse, but are just strong enough to prevent continued expansion, so the Universe will eventually reach a stable size.

**If you need to
revise this
subject more
thoroughly,
see the relevant
topics in the
*Letts* GCSE
Physics Study
Guide or
CD-ROM.**

All circular motion involves a change in velocity and, therefore, an acceleration towards the centre of the circle. The size of the acceleration increases with increasing speed and decreases with increasing radius of the circle. It is calculated using the equation $a = v^2/r$. The unbalanced force required to cause this acceleration is $F = mv^2/r$. In the case of a satellite, this unbalanced force is the gravitational pull of the planet on the satellite.

**1** The table gives some information about each of the five outer planets.

| Planet | Radius/ km | Mass (Earth = 1) | Density /g per cm³ | Surface gravitational field strength/N per kg | Surface temperature /°C | Radius of orbit (Earth = 1) | Orbital speed/ km per s |
|---|---|---|---|---|---|---|---|
| Jupiter | 71 000 | 318 | 1.33 | 23 | -150 | 5.2 | 13.1 |
| Saturn | 60 000 | 95 | 0.71 | 8.9 | -180 | 9.5 | 9.6 |
| Uranus | 25 500 | 15 | 1.24 | 8.7 | -215 | 19.1 | 6.8 |
| Neptune | 24 800 | 17 | 1.67 | 11 | -220 | 30 | |
| Pluto | 1120 | 0.025 | 1.95 | 0.72 | -225 | 39.5 | 4.7 |

(a) Describe the relationship between the surface temperature of a planet and its distance from the Sun.

.................................................................................................................................... (1)

(b) Which two planets are similar in size and mass?

.................................................................................................................................... (1)

(c) Which two planets are the closest together?

.................................................................................................................................... (1)

(d) Explain why Neptune is more massive than Uranus, even though it is smaller.

.................................................................................................................................... (1)

(e) If it were possible to land an astronaut on each planet, on which planet would the astronaut find it very difficult to jump ? Give the reason for your answer.

....................................................................................................................................

.................................................................................................................................... (2)

(f) Use the data to draw a graph of orbital speed (y axis) against radius of orbit (x axis).

(3)

(g) Use your graph to deduce the orbital speed of Neptune.

.................................................................................................................................... (1)

**2** Our Sun is a small star in its main sequence.

(a) Describe the reaction taking place in the core of the Sun.

........................................................................................................................................

.................................................................................................................... (2)

(b) It is likely that at the end of its main sequence the Sun will expand.

Describe how the colour and temperature of the Sun are likely to change as it expands.

........................................................................................................................................

.................................................................................................................... (2)

(c) After the expansion, the Sun is likely to contract again.

(i)  What causes a sun to contract?

.................................................................................................................... (1)

(ii) Describe what is likely to happen to the Sun after it has contracted.

........................................................................................................................................

.................................................................................................................... (2)

**3** Comets, like the planets, go round the Sun in elliptical orbits. The orbit times of comets range from a few years to millions of years. The diagram shows a comet orbit.

○ Sun

(a) Describe and explain how the speed of a comet changes as it approaches the Sun.

........................................................................................................................................

.................................................................................................................... (2)

(b) Mark an 's' on the diagram at the point where you would expect the comet to have its smallest speed. (1)

(c) Comets have a structure similar to that of the moons of the outer planets, mainly ice. Comets become visible as a glow when their distance from the Sun is approximately three times the radius of the Earth's orbit.

(i) Suggest what is happening to a glowing comet to make it visible.

...................................................................................................................

............................................................................................... (2)

(ii) Describe how you would expect the mass of a comet to change as it finishes one complete orbit around the Sun.

...................................................................................................................

............................................................................................... (2)

(d) Comets leave trails of dust in their wake as they pass close to the Sun. Bright lights can be seen in the Earth's atmosphere when the Earth passes through these dust clouds. Suggest what happens to cause these bright lights.

...................................................................................................................

............................................................................................... (2)

4  Astronomers can measure the speed at which galaxies are moving away from the Milky Way.

(a) Explain how astronomers measure the speed of a galaxy relative to the Milky Way.

...................................................................................................................

............................................................................................... (2)

(b) How does the speed of a galaxy relative to the Milky Way depend on its distance from the Milky Way?

............................................................................................... (1)

(c) Explain how changes in the rate at which the Universe is expanding could give astronomers a clue to its future.

...................................................................................................................

...................................................................................................................

............................................................................................... (3)

**QUESTIONS**

5   The graph shows how the orbit time of an artificial satellite depends on its height above the Earth's surface.

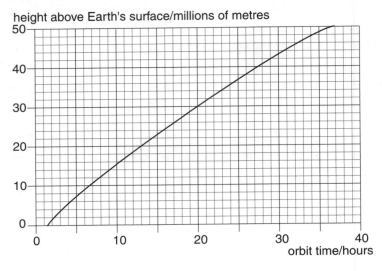

height above Earth's surface/millions of metres

(a) How does the orbit time change with increasing height above the Earth's surface?

..................................................................................................................................................

.......................................................................................................................................... (1)

(b) Some communications satellites are geostationary. They remain above the same point on the Earth's surface.

   (i)  Write down the orbit time of a geostationary satellite.

   .......................................................................................................................................... (1)

   (ii) Use the graph to find the height above the Earth's surface of a geostationary satellite.

   .......................................................................................................................................... (1)

(c) Some weather satellites occupy very low orbits, close to the surface of the Earth. Describe **two** advantages of a low orbit for a weather satellite.

   1 ..............................................................................................................................................

   ................................................................................................................................................

   ................................................................................................................................................

   2 ..............................................................................................................................................

   ................................................................................................................................................

........................................................................................................................... (2)

*Edexcel 1998*

Nothing can happen without an energy transfer. A braking car is transferring **kinetic** energy into **thermal** energy or **heat**. When a car accelerates, **chemical** energy from the fuel is being transferred into kinetic energy, but a car travelling at a constant speed on the level is just transferring chemical energy into thermal energy of the surroundings!

Devices such as heaters, lamps, television sets and radios are designed to carry out a particular energy transfer. A gas fire is designed to transfer chemical energy from the gas into thermal energy and a lamp is designed to transfer energy from electricity into light. Although all the energy that goes into one of these devices must come out (this is known as conservation of energy – the total amount of energy remains the same), it does not all come out in the desired form.

Tungsten filament lamps are poor at achieving the desired energy transfer, typically producing about 5 J of light for every 100 J energy supplied from electricity.

Modern fluorescent lamps are more efficient; they transfer more of the energy input into the desired output, i.e. light. The efficiency of a device is the fraction or percentage of the energy input that is output in a useful form. Filament lamps have an efficiency of about 5%, whereas that of fluorescent lamps is about 20%.

There are four mechanisms by which energy from hot objects, such as lamps and heaters, is lost to the surroundings. First, everything emits **infra-red radiation**. The rate of emission increases with increasing temperature and depends on the nature of the surface. A dull, dark surface emits more radiation than a shiny one at the same temperature. The dark surface is also a better absorber than the shiny one. Aluminium foil and silvered surfaces are used as insulators because they reflect infra-red radiation, so they can reduce the amount of heat leaving a hot object or entering a cold one.

A second mechanism is by **conduction** – the transfer of energy from an energetic molecule to a less energetic one when they collide. Conduction in metals is a more rapid process than in non-metals because the free electrons diffuse within the metal, spreading the energy around. Gases are poor conductors of thermal energy, because of the relatively large spacing between the particles compared to a liquid or a solid.

The third mechanism is by **convection currents**, which only occur in fluids. They are caused by differences in density when part of the fluid is warmed or cooled. Convection currents keep the air circulating in a refrigerator and in a room that is heated by a 'radiator'.

Fourth, liquids and objects that contain moisture can also lose energy by **evaporation**. When this happens the more energetic particles leave the surface of the liquid. Thus, the average energy of the particles remaining in the liquid is reduced, causing the liquid to cool.

Insulation is most effective when it targets the main form of energy transfer. Warm objects, such as people and their houses, lose most energy by conduction and convection. They can be insulated by trapping layers of air in such things as clothing and cavity wall insulation. Air is a poor conductor, but it needs to be trapped to stop energy transfer by convection currents.

Hot, moist objects, such as food taken from an oven, lose most energy by radiation and evaporation. Covering food with aluminium foil is an effective way of keeping it warm for short periods of time.

Most of the energy that we transfer in our homes comes from fossil fuels. Energy from the Sun was trapped millions of years ago and stored as **chemical** energy. Fossil fuels are **non-renewable** – we cannot make any more coal, gas or oil. Nuclear fission fuels, such as uranium, are also non-renewable. Some electricity is generated from renewable sources: **hydroelectric power** uses energy from the Sun that drives the water cycle and **wind** power uses energy from the Sun that causes movement of airstreams. Solar cells transfer energy from the Sun directly into electricity, but their high cost and low efficiency give them limited use in Britain.

Our bodies use **renewable** energy sources. Plants transfer energy from the Sun into chemical energy or **biomass**. Unlike the formation of coal, this is a short-term process and one that can be repeated many times in a short timescale.

**REVISION SUMMARY**

Cost is an important factor when choosing an energy source and this is often governed by availability. Environmental factors are increasingly being taken into account. Although wind 'farms' do not cause the atmospheric pollution associated with fossil fuels, some people do regard them as being noisy and ugly. Social factors to be taken into account include employment and environmental changes that could affect tourism or the livelihood of a community.

Forces that cause movement are doing work and transferring energy. The amount of work done, or energy transferred, is calculated using the formula:

work done = force × distance moved in direction of force
or in symbols $W = Fd$

Work and energy are measured in **joules** (J).

The rate at which work is done, or energy is transferred, is called the **power**. This is the work done by a force each second and is measured in **watts** (W). Power is calculated using the formula:

$$\text{power} = \frac{\text{work done/energy transfer}}{\text{time taken}} \qquad \text{or in symbols} \quad P = \frac{E}{t}$$

Using a force to lift an object vertically is an example of transferring energy to **gravitational potential energy** (gpe). The gpe gained by the object is calculated using the formula:

change in gpe = weight × change in height or in symbols $gpe = mg\Delta h$

The symbol g stands for the gravitational field strength which is the weight of each kg of material. The gravitational field strength at the surface of the Earth is about 10 N/kg and that at the surface of the Moon is about 1.5 N/kg.

When an object changes speed its **kinetic energy** (ke) changes. The formula for kinetic energy is:

$$\text{kinetic energy} = \tfrac{1}{2} \times \text{mass} \times (\text{velocity})^2 \qquad \text{or in symbols} \quad ke = \tfrac{1}{2}mv^2$$

For an object moving vertically in the absence of air resistance, the energy transfer is between gravitational potential energy and ke, so the change in gpe is equal to the change in ke.

**If you need to revise this subject more thoroughly, see the relevant topics in the *Letts* GCSE Physics Study Guide or CD-ROM.**

The amount of energy absorbed or released when an object heats up or cools down depends on the temperature change, the quantity of material and its **specific heat capacity**. The specific heat capacity is the energy transfer needed to change the temperature of 1 kg of material by 1°C or 1K. The equation is:

energy change = mass × specific heat capacity × temperature change
or in symbols $\Delta E = mc\Delta T$

1 (a) Some of the jobs listed below involve an energy transfer and some do not. Place a tick in the box at the side of those that involve transfer of energy.

☐ A man pushing a supermarket trolley.

☐ A girl pedalling a bicycle.

☐ A shelf supporting some books.

☐ A gas flame heating some water.

☐ The weight of a building pushing down on the ground.

☐ Water evaporating from the sea.

☐ The upward push of the sea on a floating ship.

☐ The upward push of the atmosphere on a rising hot-air balloon.                (8)

(b) Modern 'energy-efficient' lamps produce the same light output as tungsten filament lamps for less electrical energy input. The following diagram is an incomplete picture of the energy flow through an 'energy-efficient' lamp in one second.

| 25 J energy from electricity | → | Energy-efficient lamp | → | 6 J energy as light |
| | | | ↘ | |

Complete the diagram by writing the amount and type of energy in the blank box.        (2)

2 The diagram illustrates some energy sources.

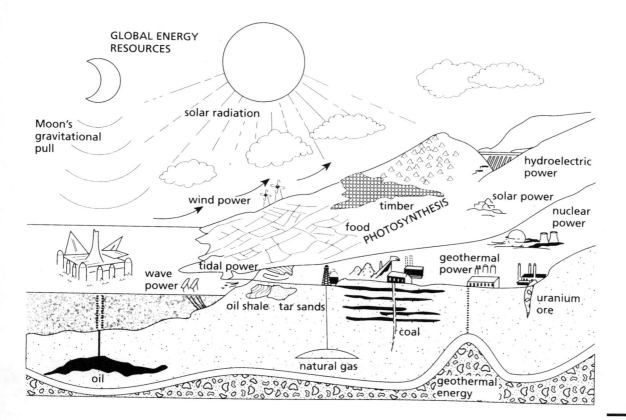

(a) (i) List **four** energy sources that are non-renewable.

.......................................................................................................................................................

....................................................................................................................................... (4)

(ii) List **four** energy sources that are renewable.

.......................................................................................................................................................

....................................................................................................................................... (4)

(iii) Which energy source stores energy from the Sun as gravitational potential energy?

....................................................................................................................................... (1)

(iv) Name **two** energy sources that store energy from the Sun as chemical energy.

....................................................................................................................................... (2)

(b) Solar power is unreliable in Britain, but in some countries many houses use energy from the Sun to produce hot water for domestic use. The diagram shows how this can be done.

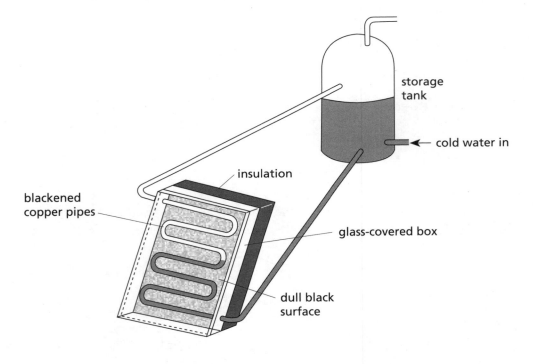

(i) Explain why the pipes are painted black.

....................................................................................................................................... (1)

(ii) State **two** reasons why copper pipes are used rather than iron pipes.

.................................................................................................................

................................................................................................................. (2)

(iii) Explain why the pipes are contained in a glass-covered box.

.................................................................................................................

................................................................................................................. (2)

(iv) Describe and explain how the water circulates in the system.

.................................................................................................................

.................................................................................................................

................................................................................................................. (3)

3   In some exposed parts of Britain the wind blows all the time. 'Wind farms' consisting of
    many wind turbines can produce as much electricity as a small coal-fired power station. A
    typical wind turbine has an electrical power output of 3 MW (1 MW = $1 \times 10^6$ W).

(a) The power of the wind blowing through the turbine is 9 MW. Use the equation:

    efficiency = useful power output ÷ total power input

    to calculate the efficiency of the turbine when the power output is 3 MW.

.................................................................................................................

................................................................................................................. (2)

(b) One disadvantage of wind turbines is the high cost of manufacture and installation. State
    **three** advantages of wind turbines over a coal-fired power station.

.................................................................................................................

.................................................................................................................

................................................................................................................. (3)

(c) State **two** other disadvantages of using wind turbines to generate electricity.

.................................................................................................................

................................................................................................................. (2)

4  The diagram shows the inside of a refrigerator.

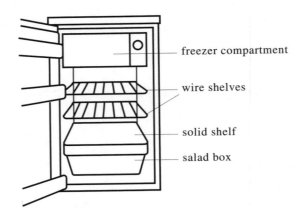

(a) Explain how the refrigerator is cooled by convection currents.

......................................................................................................................................

......................................................................................................................................

.................................................................................................................... (3)

(b) Why are wire shelves used rather than solid shelves in the centre of the refrigerator?

.................................................................................................................... (1)

(c) The refrigerator walls are insulated using both expanded polystyrene and aluminium foil.

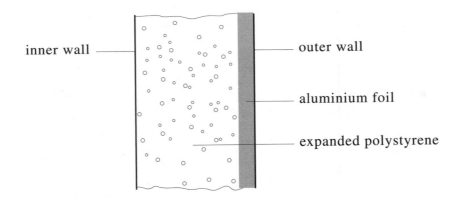

Explain how these reduce the energy entering the refrigerator.

......................................................................................................................................

.................................................................................................................... (2)

(d) The freezer compartment of the refrigerator is cooled by the forced evaporation of a liquid in the pipes.

Explain how evaporation of this liquid cools the freezer compartment.

.................................................................................................................

................................................................................................... (2)

5 (a) The diagram shows part of the roller coaster recently opened in Blackpool.

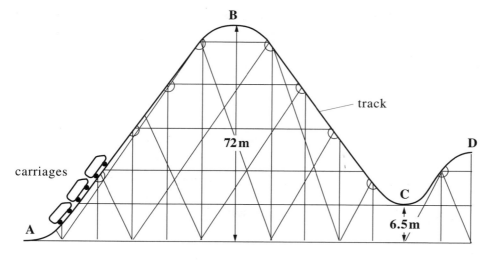

The carriages are pulled up to point B by an electric motor. Once a carriage is at Point B, it is released and free-wheels down the track towards Point C.

(i) The total mass of carriage and passengers is 3100 kg. How much gravitational potential energy will be gained in moving from Point A to Point B? (Take $g$ = 10 N/kg.)

.................................................................................................................

.................................................................................................................

................................................................................................... (3)

(ii) The power rating of the electric motor is a constant 50 kW. Calculate the time it would take for the carriage and passengers to move from Point A to Point B.

.................................................................................................................

.................................................................................................................

................................................................................................... (3)

(iii) In practice, the time taken to reach Point B will be longer than you have calculated. Explain why.

...............................................................................................................................

.......................................................................................................................... (2)

(b) (i) On release from Point B, the carriage moves down towards Point C. Describe the main energy transfer taking place as it does so.

.......................................................................................................................... (1)

(ii) By using energy considerations, calculate the maximum possible speed of the carriage as it passes through Point C.

...............................................................................................................................

...............................................................................................................................

...............................................................................................................................

.......................................................................................................................... (4)

(iii) Give **two** reasons why the height of the next peak at D has to be less than that at B.

...............................................................................................................................

.......................................................................................................................... (2)

*Edexcel 1996*

**6**  A car cooling system contains 6.3 litres of water. Each litre has a mass of 1.0 kg and the specific heat capacity of the water is $4200 \, \text{J} \, \text{kg}^{-1} \, {}^{\circ}\text{C}^{-1}$. On a cold day, the engine is started at a temperature of 5 °C and it reaches normal operating temperature at 95 °C. Calculate the energy absorbed by the water while the car is 'warming up'.

...............................................................................................................................

...............................................................................................................................

.......................................................................................................................... (3)

Radiation is all around us in the form of **background radiation**. Some of this comes from space, some from rocks and some from the radioactive carbon in us and every other living thing. Radioactive decay occurs when an unstable nucleus emits energy in the form of electromagnetic radiation or a particle when it changes to a more stable nucleus. The table summarises the three main types of radiation that can be emitted.

| Type of nuclear radiation | Nature | Charge | Penetration | Ionising ability |
|---|---|---|---|---|
| **Alpha** | two neutrons and two protons, sometimes referred to as a helium nucleus | positive | stopped by a few cm of air or a thin piece of card | intensely ionising |
| **Beta** | high-speed electron emitted when a neutron decays to a proton and an electron | negative | partially absorbed by aluminium foil; totally absorbed by 5 mm aluminium | less than alpha; ionisation occurs at collisions with atoms and molecules |
| **Gamma** | high-frequency, short-wavelength electromagnetic radiation | none | never totally absorbed; intensity is reduced by thick lead or concrete | weakly ionising; the high penetration is due to few collisions where ionisation would occur |

Many elements exist in different forms called **isotopes**, some of which are more stable than others. The different isotopes of an element have the same electron arrangement and the same number of protons, but differ in the number of neutrons. The most common form of carbon is carbon-12 (the 12 refers to the total number of protons and neutrons). However, the isotope carbon-14, an unstable form of carbon, also exists in nature. The table compares the isotopes.

| Isotope | Electron arrangement | Number of protons | Number of neutrons |
|---|---|---|---|
| carbon-12 | 2, 4 | 6 | 6 |
| carbon-14 | 2, 4 | 6 | 8 |

When carbon-14 decays, it emits a beta particle as a neutron, becomes a proton and the atom changes to a nitrogen atom.

$$^{14}_{6}\text{C} \rightarrow {}^{14}_{7}\text{N} + {}^{0}_{-1}\text{e}$$

Note that in the symbolic equation the top number to the left of the atomic symbol represents the **mass number**, or total number of protons and neutrons, and the bottom number is the **atomic number**, or number of protons.

Carbon-14 decays with a **half-life** of 5730 years. This means that, on average, half of the carbon-14 atoms in a sample of carbon change to nitrogen during this time. After one half-life of a material half of the unstable atoms are still present and the rate of decay has halved. These numbers halve again to a quarter of the original value after a second half-life and so on.

All living things contain a constant proportion of carbon-14. When they die, they stop taking in new supplies of carbon-14 and so the proportion goes down as the carbon-14 decays. The time since the death of plant or animal material can be estimated by measuring the proportion of carbon-14 present and calculating the number of half-lives that have elapsed since death. This is a technique known as **radio-carbon dating**.

Substances with a long half-life, such as uranium-238 which has a half-life of 4500 million years, can be used to date rocks. Uranium-238 decays to lead, enabling the age of a rock to be estimated from the proportions of lead and uranium-238 present.

Radioactive isotopes are widely used in medicine for detecting and treating illness, for killing bacteria and for tracing the movement of fluids.

Nuclear power relies on the energy released when a large, unstable nucleus is split, or 'fissioned', into smaller ones. The splitting of the nucleus is triggered when a neutron is absorbed. As well as energy, other neutrons are released which can go on to cause more fissions.

Changing the pressure of a gas causes its volume to change. Provided that the amount of gas and its temperature are unchanged, the pressure is inversely proportional to the volume. This means that if one of the quantities is doubled, the other one halves. This is known as **Boyle's law** and can be written as:

$$\text{pressure} \times \text{volume} = \text{constant} \qquad \text{or in symbols} \qquad P_1 V_1 = P_2 V_2$$

If the temperature of a gas is changed, while the volume and the amount of gas remain the same, the change in pressure is described by the pressure law

$$\frac{\text{pressure}}{\text{temperature}} = \text{constant} \qquad \text{or in symbols} \qquad \frac{P_1}{T_1} = \frac{P_2}{T_2}$$

To use this relationship, the temperature must be measured on the kelvin scale of temperature. A temperature in degrees celsius (°C) is converted to a temperature in kelvin (K) by adding 273.

Combining the pressure law with Boyle's law gives the general gas equation:

$$\frac{\text{pressure} \times \text{volume}}{\text{temperature}} = \text{constant} \qquad \text{or in symbols} \qquad \frac{P_1 V_1}{T_1} = \frac{P_2 V_2}{T_2}$$

The **kinetic theory** uses our understanding of the behaviour of individual **atoms** and **molecules** to explain the properties of materials made up of large numbers of atoms and molecules. Important evidence that molecules are constantly moving comes from the observation of larger particles suspended in air or water. Smoke specks in air and carbon specks in water can be seen to move in an erratic, jerky motion. This movement is called **Brownian motion** after Robert Brown, the person who is credited with first observing it. The explanation for Brownian motion is that the specks must be subjected to bombardment and, as the bombarding particles are much smaller than the specks, they must be moving at very high speeds.

This gives a picture of gas molecules as being in constant rapid, unordered motion, making frequent collisions with other molecules and the walls of the containing vessel. Liquids are denser than gases and are pictured as being more closely packed with less freedom of movement. Their motion can be described as 'jostling'.

Solids have a fixed shape due to the molecules being in fixed positions, but the molecules in a solid are not 'still'. Their motion is a constant vibration at high frequency.

**Temperature** is a measure of the energy of the molecular movement. The higher the temperature, the more energy the molecules have.

**Diffusion** is the name given to the process whereby substances mix together when placed in contact. Diffusion in gases is a rapid process – cooking smells travel quickly – but diffusion in liquids and solids is much slower, because the molecules only travel short distances between collisions.

Unlike solids and liquids, gases are squashy because of the large spacing between molecules. Most of the volume occupied by a gas at room temperature is free space, and the molecules can be pushed into this space. Gas pressure is due to collisions between the molecules and the container walls.

**1** (a) The table gives details of three types of nuclear radiation. Complete it by identifying the radiations.

| Type | Nature | Penetrating power | Charge |
|---|---|---|---|
| | Electromagnetic radiation | Absorbed by thick lead | 0 |
| | Helium nuclei | Stopped by paper | +2 |
| | Fast moving electrons | Stopped by 3 mm aluminium | −1 |

(3)

(b) In a paper mill, large rollers are used to determine the thickness of the paper as shown in the diagram.

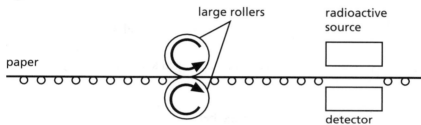

(i) A radioactive source may be used to monitor the thickness of the paper. The readings over a period of time are given below.

| Time (minutes) | 1 | 2 | 3 | 4 | 5 | 6 | 7 | 8 |
|---|---|---|---|---|---|---|---|---|
| Corrected count rate (counts per second) | 55 | 55 | 55 | 58 | 60 | 60 | 60 | 60 |

What do these results tell the person operating the paper mill? Explain your answer.

..............................................................................................................................................

.................................................................................................................. (2)

(ii) From the list below put a tick by the most suitable source for this purpose.

| Radioactive source | Half-life | Type of radiation |
|---|---|---|
| $^{24}$Na | 15 hours | Gamma |
| $^{131}$I | 8 days | Beta and Gamma |
| $^{90}$Sr | 28 years | Beta |
| $^{214}$Am | 433 years | Alpha |
| $^{235}$U | 700 000 000 years | Alpha |

(1)

(iii) Explain why you chose this source.

.......................................................................................................................................

.......................................................................................................................................

.......................................................................................................................................

....................................................................................................................... (4)

(c) One danger associated with nuclear radiation is that it can damage living cells. How can this danger be minimised?

.......................................................................................................................................

.......................................................................................................................................

.......................................................................................................................................

....................................................................................................................... (4)

*Edexcel 1995*

2 Radioactive materials are used in hospitals as tracers. The isotope commonly used is technetium-99. This is attached to another chemical, so that it is directed to the organ being investigated. The radioactive tracer is injected into the patient's bloodstream and, after a short time, a photograph is taken to show its distribution in the body. Technetium-99 emits gamma radiation.

(a) Explain why gamma is a suitable radiation to use for this purpose.

........................................................................................................................

.................................................................................................................... (2)

(b) Describe the dangers to a patient if an alpha- or beta-emitter were used instead.

........................................................................................................................

........................................................................................................................

.................................................................................................................... (3)

(c) When choosing a radioactive material for a particular purpose, the half-life has to be considered.

   (i) Describe the meaning of the term 'half-life'.

     ........................................................................................................

     .................................................................................................... (2)

   (ii) Technetium-99 has a half-life of 6 hours. Suggest why this is a suitable half-life for tracers used in medicine.

     ........................................................................................................

     .................................................................................................... (2)

3 A carbon dioxide cylinder contains $300\,\text{cm}^3$ of gas at a pressure of $2.40 \times 10^7\,\text{Pa}$. Atmospheric pressure is $1.01 \times 10^5\,\text{Pa}$.

(a) Explain why the cylinder walls are thick cast iron.

.................................................................................................................... (1)

(b) Calculate the volume of the gas at atmospheric pressure.

................................................................................................................

................................................................................................................

................................................................................................................ (3)

(c) The cylinder valve is opened and the gas that emerges is collected.
What volume of gas is collected?

................................................................................................................ (1)

4   A balloon seller has a cylinder of helium gas which he uses to blow up his balloons.

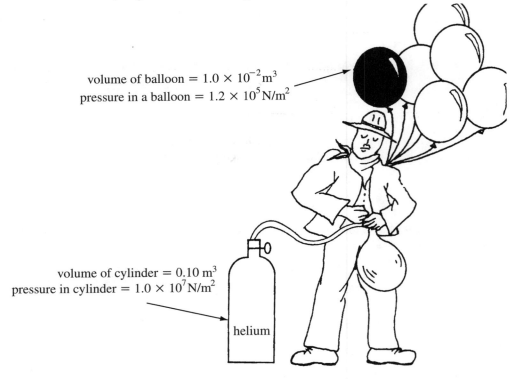

volume of balloon = $1.0 \times 10^{-2} \, \text{m}^3$
pressure in a balloon = $1.2 \times 10^5 \, \text{N/m}^2$

volume of cylinder = $0.10 \, \text{m}^3$
pressure in cylinder = $1.0 \times 10^7 \, \text{N/m}^2$

helium

The volume of the cylinder is $0.10 \, \text{m}^3$. It contains helium gas at a pressure of $1.0 \times 10^7 \, \text{N/m}^2$. The balloon seller fills each balloon to a volume of $1.0 \times 10^{-2} \, \text{m}^3$ and a pressure of $1.2 \times 10^5 \, \text{N/m}^2$.

(a) Explain in terms of particles, how the helium in the cylinder produces a pressure.

................................................................................................................

................................................................................................................

................................................................................................................ (2)

(b) Calculate the total volume that the helium gas will occupy at a pressure of $1.2 \times 10^5 \, \text{N/m}^2$. You can assume that there is no change in the temperature of the helium gas.

..............................................................................................................................

..............................................................................................................................

..............................................................................................................................

.......................................................................................................... (3)

(c) Calculate the number of balloons of volume $1.0 \times 10^{-2} \, \text{m}^3$ that the balloon seller can fill using the gas. Use the formula $P_1 V_1 = P_2 V_2$.

..............................................................................................................................

..............................................................................................................................

.......................................................................................................... (2)

*Edexcel 1998*

---

5 Smoke particles in air can be observed using a low power microscope. They move in an erratic way. The diagram shows the path of a smoke particle in air.

(a) Describe the motion of the smoke particle.

..............................................................................................................................

.......................................................................................................... (2)

(b) Explain how the movement of the smoke particle provides evidence about the motion of air particles.

..............................................................................................................................

..............................................................................................................................

..............................................................................................................................

.......................................................................................................... (4)

*Try to complete this paper in a single sitting of **one and a half hours**.*

**1** The table shows how the length of a spring changes when different loads are applied.

| load in N | length in cm |
|-----------|--------------|
| 0.5 | 6.0 |
| 1.0 | 8.5 |
| 2.0 | 13.5 |
| 2.5 | 16.0 |
| 3.0 | 20.0 |

(a) Use the grid to plot these points and draw the best line. (3)

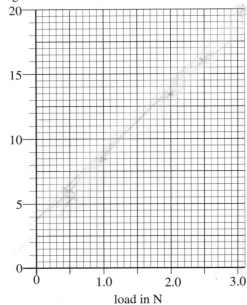

(b) Write down the length of the spring for a load of 1.5 N.

............................................................................................................................................................ (1)

(c) How long is the spring with no load?

............................................................................................................................................................ (1)

(d) For what range of forces is the extension proportional to the force?
Explain how you can tell.

............................................................................................................................................................

............................................................................................................................................................ (2)

2  When travelling on a motorway, a motorist maintains an average speed of 60 mph.

(a) Calculate the time it takes to complete a 270 mile journey at this average speed.

................................................................................................................ (3)

(b) A speed of 60 mph is equivalent to 30 m/s.
Calculate the kinetic energy of a 900 kg car and driver travelling at this speed.

................................................................................................................ (3)

(c) In an emergency stop, kinetic energy is removed at the rate of 67.5 kW
(1 kW = 1000 W). Calculate the time it takes to bring the car to a halt.

................................................................................................................ (3)

(d) How far does the car travel while the driver is braking?

................................................................................................................ (3)

(e) When the car is fully laden with three passengers and their luggage, the mass of the car
is 200 kg more than in (b).
Explain how this affects the braking distance of the car.

................................................................................................................

................................................................................................................ (2)

3   The diagram shows how light travels in a curved optical fibre.

(a) Explain why light does not pass through the edges of the fibre.

..............................................................................................................................

.......................................................................................................................... (2)

(b) Describe how optical fibres are used in medicine.

..............................................................................................................................

..............................................................................................................................

.......................................................................................................................... (3)

4      The diagram represents sound waves approaching a doorway.

(a) Draw in the wavefronts after the sound has passed through the doorway.          (2)

(b) Write down the name of this effect.

.......................................................................................................................... (1)

(c) Explain how the behaviour of a beam of light waves passing through a doorway is different to that of sound waves.

..............................................................................................................................

.......................................................................................................................... (2)

5      Planets, moons, asteroids and comets are all objects in the Solar System.

(a) Describe the differences between planet and a moon.

..............................................................................................................................

..............................................................................................................................

.......................................................................................................................... (2)

(b) Describe the differences between the orbits of the planets and the orbits of comets.

..................................................................................................

..................................................................................................

.............................................................................................. (4)

(c) Whereabouts in the Solar System are the asteroids?

.............................................................................................. (2)

Our Sun is a star that is thought to have formed in a dust cloud that was left over from an exploding supernova.

(d) Describe and explain the events that cause a supernova to explode.

..................................................................................................

.............................................................................................. (3)

(e) Describe how stars form in clouds of dust.

..................................................................................................

.............................................................................................. (3)

(f) What is the source of energy that radiates from stars?

..................................................................................................

.............................................................................................. (2)

(g) Describe what is likely to happen to our Sun at the end of its main sequence.

..................................................................................................

.............................................................................................. (3)

6   The coolant in a refrigerator transfers energy from the inside to the outside. It evaporates as it passes through the pipes inside the freezer compartment.
On the outside of the refrigerator, the vapour is compressed back into a liquid which then cools as it passes through the pipes mounted at the back of the refrigerator.

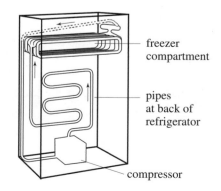

freezer compartment

pipes at back of refrigerator

compressor

(a) Explain how the freezer compartment is cooled.

..................................................................................................................

.......................................................................................................... (2)

(b) The pipes at the back of the refrigerator are coloured black. Explain how this helps to cool the warm liquid that passes through them.

..................................................................................................................

.......................................................................................................... (2)

(c) Explain how movement of air at the back of the refrigerator also cools the warm liquid.

..................................................................................................................

.......................................................................................................... (3)

(d) The manufacturers recommend that a minimum five centimetre gap is left between the pipes at the back of the refrigerator and the wall of the room. Explain why this is necessary and suggest what is likely to happen if a smaller gap is used.

..................................................................................................................

.......................................................................................................... (3)

7  Here are three descriptions of the main types of nuclear radiation.
   **A**  Short wavelength electromagnetic radiation.
   **B**  A particle consisting of two protons and two neutrons.
   **C**  A fast-moving electron.

(a) Which lettered statement is a description of:

   (i)  An alpha particle?.................................................................................... (1)

   (ii)  A beta particle?...................................................................................... (1)

   (iii) Gamma radiation? .................................................................................. (1)

Radon-220 is a radioactive gas that seeps from underground rocks. It decays by emitting alpha particles and it has a half-life of 52 s.

(b) Explain the meaning of the term half-life.

..................................................................................................................

.......................................................................................................... (2)

(c) The activity of a sample of radon-220 is measured to be 520 counts/s.
   (i)  Name a suitable instrument for measuring the activity of the radon-220.

...................................................................................................................... (1)

   (ii) Estimate the activity of the radon-220 after

   52 s ...................................104 s.................................................... (2)

   (iii) Explain why it is not possible to make a precise prediction of the activity of the
        radon gas.

..........................................................................................................................

...................................................................................................................... (2)

**8**  The diagram shows a relay, an
   electromagnetically operated switch.

   (a) The coil has a resistance of 240 Ω.
       Calculate the current in the coil when it
       is connected to a 6 V supply.

*Diagram labels: pivot; coil wound on iron core; L-shaped iron armature; low-voltage d.c. source; switch contacts; 240 V a.c.; mains lamp*

..........................................................................................................................

...................................................................................................................... (3)

   (b) Explain how the mains lamp becomes switched on when current passes in the relay coil.

..........................................................................................................................

..........................................................................................................................

...................................................................................................................... (4)

   (c) Describe one advantage of using a relay in switching.

...................................................................................................................... (1)

# Answers

## 1 ELECTRICITY AND MAGNETISM

| Question | Answer | Mark |
|---|---|---|
| 1 (a) | The spray gun takes electrons away. | 1 |
| (b) | All the drops have the same type of charge (positive). | 1 |
| | Similar charges repel each other. | 1 |

> **Examiner's tip** Candidates often lose marks because they do not give a full explanation. In this case, many candidates would not gain the second mark, being content to make the first statement only. When two marks are available for an answer, two separate points usually have to be made.

| | | |
|---|---|---|
| (c) | Negative. | 1 |
| (d) | Charged drops are attracted to the plants. | 1 |
| | This results in less waste OR all the plant is covered with insecticide. | 1 |

> **Examiner's tip** One advantage of using charged drops for spraying plants or charged particles of paint for spraying metal panels is that the charge ensures complete coverage, because the drops or paint are attracted to all parts of the plant or metal panel.

| | | |
|---|---|---|
| 2 (a) | A1 reads 0.15 A. | 1 |
| | A2 reads 1.8 A. | 1 |
| | A3 reads 0.6 A. | 1 |
| | A4 reads 1.8 A. | 1 |

> **Examiner's tip** This question is testing whether you know the rules for current in circuits. In a series circuit the current is the same at all parts of the circuit. None is used up by the components. When a circuit has components in parallel, the sum of the currents in the individual branches is equal to current passing into the junction.

| | | |
|---|---|---|
| (b) | V1 reads 3.7 V. | 1 |
| | V2 reads 3.7 V. | 1 |

> **Examiner's tip** Components in parallel always have the same voltage across them.

| | | |
|---|---|---|
| 3 (a) | B is the best conductor. | 1 |
| | Because it needs the smallest voltage to cause the same current. | 1 |
| (b) | Knowledge that $R = V \div I$ | 1 |
| | $= 0.6\,V \div 0.8\,A$ | 1 |
| | $= 0.75\,\Omega$ | 1 |

> **Examiner's tip** You must have the correct unit for the third mark. If your answer is 0.75 with no unit or the wrong unit, you gain two marks out of the three. Although you would usually gain full marks for the correct answer with no working, showing your working allows you to gain some credit, e.g. for knowledge of the formula, even if your final answer is wrong.

| Question | Answer | Mark |
|---|---|---|
| (c) | Knowledge of the formula $P = I \times V$ | 1 |
| | The power in wire A $\quad P = 0.8\,\text{A} \times 5.2\,\text{V}$ | 1 |
| | $= 4.16\,\text{W}$ | 1 |
| | Similarly for wire B, $P = 0.48\,\text{W}$, and for C, $P = 9.92\,\text{W}$. | 1 |
| | C gets hottest because it has the greatest power. | 1 |

**Examiner's tip** When you are asked to 'explain why', you must give a reason. The reason in this case is 'because it has the greatest power'.

| | | |
|---|---|---|
| (d) | Knowledge of the formula $Q = It$ | 1 |
| | For each wire $Q = 0.8\,\text{A} \times 60\,\text{s}$ | 1 |
| | $= 48\,\text{C}$ | 1 |

**Examiner's tip** As the wires carry the same current, the same quantity of charge flows through each in one minute. For the formula to be valid, the current must be in amps and the time in seconds.

| | | |
|---|---|---|
| 4 (a) | $I = P \div V$ | 1 |
| | $= 60\,\text{W} \div 230\,\text{V}$ | 1 |
| | $= 0.26\,\text{A}$ | 1 |

**Examiner's tip** Full marks are awarded for the correct answer and unit. If you do not show the working, you cannot gain marks for a partially correct answer. In this case, you could have inadvertently keyed into your calculator '230 ÷ 60'. Writing down an incorrect answer of 3.83 A would gain no marks, but the correct working followed by the wrong answer would gain two marks out of three.

| | | |
|---|---|---|
| (b) | Current in lamp B = 0.50 A | 1 |
| | $R = V \div I$ | 1 |
| | $= 230\,\text{V} \div 0.50\,\text{A}$ | 1 |
| | $= 460\,\Omega$ | 1 |

**Examiner's tip** If you arrived at the correct numerical answer, but had the wrong unit or no unit, award yourself three marks out of four.
You also gain three marks out of four if you did not work out the current in lamp B correctly, but made no other errors.

| | | |
|---|---|---|
| (c) | The fuse wire melts | 1 |
| | if the current exceeds the fuse rating. | 1 |
| | This protects the wires from overheating. | 1 |

| | | |
|---|---|---|
| 5 (a) | Current in the coil creates a magnetic field, | 1 |
| | this magnetises the iron core, | 1 |
| | the iron bar is attracted to the core, | 1 |
| | this pulls the steel bolt out of the door. | 1 |

**Examiner's tip** It is important to emphasise that the coil has its own magnetic field. Without the iron core, this would not be strong enough to attract the iron bar.

| Question | Answer | Mark |
|---|---|---|
| (b) | To pull the iron bar from the core when the current is switched off. | 1 |
| (c) | Yes. | 1 |
| | The iron bar is attracted to the iron core whatever its polarity. | 1 |

> **Examiner's tip** Iron is 'soft' magnetic material. It is readily magnetised in the presence of a magnetic field and quickly loses its magnetism when the field is removed.

| Question | Answer | Mark |
|---|---|---|
| 6 (a) | There is a changing magnetic field in and around the coil. | 1 |
| | This induces a voltage, which causes a current in the coil. | 1 |

> **Examiner's tip** When answering questions about electromagnetic induction, it is important to emphasise whether or not the magnetic field is changing.

| Question | Answer | Mark |
|---|---|---|
| (b) (i) | There is no reading on the ammeter | 1 |
| | because the magnetic field around the coil is not changing. | 1 |
| (ii) | The ammeter deflection is to the left | 1 |
| | because the change of field has been reversed. | 1 |

> **Examiner's tip** Note that reversing the magnet or the direction of movement causes the current to pass in the opposite direction.

| Question | Answer | Mark |
|---|---|---|
| (iii) | The current alternates, changing direction when the movement of the magnet changes direction. | 1 |
| | The current is bigger than before because the movement is faster, so the magnetic field changes at a greater rate. | 1 |

| Question | Answer | Mark |
|---|---|---|
| 7 (a) | The ratio of the voltages is 1:16. | 1 |
| | The turns ratio is the same, so the number is $16 \times 20\,000 = 320\,000$. | 1 |
| (b) | **Either** to reduce the current transmitted **or** to reduce the power losses. | 1 |

| Question | Answer | Mark |
|---|---|---|
| 8 (a) | The input sensor is the temperature sensor. | 1 |
| | The processor is the transistor switch. | 1 |
| | The output device is the relay/heater. | 1 |
| (b) | The current in the heater is too great for the transistor switch to handle. | 1 |
| | The relay enables the large current in the heater to be switched by a much smaller current. | 1 |
| (c) (i) | $9.0\,\text{V} - 0.6\,\text{V} = 8.4\,\text{V}$. | 1 |

> **Examiner's tip** Note that in a series circuit the total voltage is the sum of the voltages across the components.

| Question | Answer | Mark |
|---|---|---|
| (ii) | Knowledge of the formula $I = V \div R$ | 1 |
| | Circuit current $= 8.4\,\text{V} \div 1000\,\Omega$ | 1 |
| | $= 0.0084\,\text{A or } 8.4\,\text{mA}$ | 1 |

| Question | Answer | Mark |
|---|---|---|

Thermistor resistance $= 0.6\,V \div 0.0084\,A$
$\qquad\qquad\qquad = 71.4\,\Omega$ — **1**

(iii) The current in the thermistor has a heating effect. — **1**
This needs to be minimised, so that it does not turn the heater off even though the temperature is too low. — **1**

(d) The 9 V voltage in the sensing circuit is shared between the thermistor and the fixed resistor. — **1**
When the thermistor gets warmer, its resistance drops and its share of the voltage goes down. — **1**
The transistor switch is turned off when the voltage across the thermistor drops below 0.6 V. — **1**

**9** (a) (i) OR 0 AND 0 — **1**
(ii) OR 1 AND 1 — **1**
(iii) OR 1 AND 0 — **1**
(iv) OR 1 AND 0 — **1**

(b) Line (i). — **1**
(c) Lines (iii) and (iv). — **1**
(d) Either door A or door B has to be opened. — **1**
And the master switch has to be on. — **1**

(e) The relay enables the low current from the logic gate — **1**
to switch a higher current to the alarm. — **1**

## 2 FORCES AND MOTION

| Question | Answer | Mark |
|---|---|---|
| 1 (a) (i) | Diagram A shows a car that is accelerating forwards. | 1 |
| (ii) | Diagrams C and D show cars that are travelling forwards and slowing down. | 2 |
| (iii) | Diagram B shows a car travelling at a constant speed. | 1 |
| (b) (i) | Knowledge of formula speed = distance ÷ time | 1 |
| | = 240 m ÷ 16 s | 1 |
| | = 15 m/s | 1 |

**Examiner's tip** Note that the correct answer and unit gains full marks, but always show your working in case you make an arithmetical mistake. This allows you to be awarded partial credit, even though your final answer may be wrong. You gain two marks if you have the correct answer, but a wrong or missing unit.

| | | |
|---|---|---|
| (ii) | Rearrangement of formula to give time = distance ÷ speed | 1 |
| | = 330 000 m ÷ 15 m/s | 1 |
| | = 22 000 s | 1 |

| | | |
|---|---|---|
| 2 (a) | The acceleration is decreasing. | 1 |

**Examiner's tip** The gradient of a speed-time graph represents the acceleration. In this case, the gradient is decreasing, showing that the acceleration is also decreasing.

| | | |
|---|---|---|
| | As the parachutist speeds up, the resistive force increases. | 1 |
| | The resultant force on the parachutist decreases. | 1 |

**Examiner's tip** The resultant force is the sum of all the forces acting. In this case the parachutist's weight acts downwards and the resistive force acts upwards, so the resultant downward force is equal to (weight − resistive force).

| | | |
|---|---|---|
| (b) | $\text{acceleration} = \dfrac{\text{increase in velocity}}{\text{time taken}}$ | 1 |
| | $= \dfrac{(10\,\text{m/s} - 56\,\text{m/s})}{10\,\text{s}}$ | 1 |
| | $= -4.6\,\text{m/s}^2$ | 1 |

**Examiner's tip** The acceleration here is negative, because the velocity of the parachutist decreased. This negative acceleration is sometimes referred to as a deceleration.

| | | |
|---|---|---|
| (c) | distance travelled = average speed × time | 1 |
| | = 10 m/s × 20 s | 1 |
| | = 200 m | 1 |

| Question | Answer | Mark |
|---|---|---|
| **3** (a) (i) | 400 N | **1** |
| (ii) | Your arrow should point downwards. | **1** |

> **Examiner's tip** Friction forces oppose sliding, so the friction force is always in the opposite direction to any sliding that could occur.

| | | |
|---|---|---|
| (b) (i) | pressure = force ÷ area | **1** |
| (ii) | pressure = 8400 N ÷ 210 cm$^2$ | **1** |
| | = 40 N/cm$^2$ | **1** |

> **Examiner's tip** The pascal (Pa) is a unit of pressure but it is equivalent to 1 N/m$^2$, so it does not apply in this case unless you converted the area to 0.021 m$^2$.

| | | |
|---|---|---|
| (c) | The lift multiplies force **or** the lift enables a large force to be exerted when a small force acts at the pump. | **2** |

| | | |
|---|---|---|
| **4** (a) (i) | *One mark each for any two points from:* Tiredness or alertness of driver; whether drugs/medicines/alcohol have been taken; distractions, e.g. children in the car or hi-fi. | **2** |
| (ii) | A: increases. | **1** |
| | B: no effect. | **1** |
| | C: increases. | **1** |

> **Examiner's tip** The thinking distance is the distance travelled by the car during the reaction time. If the reaction time increases, then so does the thinking distance. However, the braking distance is not affected, since this is the distance that the car travels after the driver has reacted.

| | | |
|---|---|---|
| (b) | Water acts as a lubricant/reduces the friction forces needed for braking, so the braking distance increases. | **1** **1** |

> **Examiner's tip** Avoid ambiguous phrases, such as 'it takes longer to stop', as it is not clear whether this refers to the distance or the time.

| | | |
|---|---|---|
| (c) (i) | Deceleration = decrease in velocity ÷ time | **1** |
| | = 30 m/s ÷ 4.8 s = 6.25 (m/s$^2$) | **1** |
| (ii) | braking force = mass × deceleration | **1** |
| | = 900 kg × 6.25 m/s$^2$ = 5625 (N) | **1** |

> **Examiner's tip** Questions involving the use of the relationship *force = mass × acceleration* are very common on Higher tier papers. In this case because it is a braking force, deceleration is used instead of acceleration.

| Question | Answer | Mark |
|---|---|---|
| (iii) | distance travelled = average speed × time | 1 |
| | = 15 m/s × 4.8 s = 72 (m) | 1 |

> **Examiner's tip** Since the car decelerated uniformly from 30 m/s to 0 m/s, the average speed was 15 m/s.

| | | | | |
|---|---|---|---|---|
| **5** | (a) | (i) | There is a delay before the driver reacts (reaction time). | 1 |
| | | | This time elapses before the driver brakes. | 1 |
| | | (ii) | Knowledge of formula   distance = speed × time | 1 |
| | | | = 24 m/s × 1.2 s | 1 |
| | | | = 28.8 m | 1 |
| | | (iii) | Knowledge of formula   deceleration = decrease in speed ÷ time | 1 |
| | | | = 24 m/s ÷ 4.2 s | 1 |
| | | | = 5.7 m/s$^2$ | 1 |
| | | (iv) | Knowledge of formula   force = mass × acceleration | 1 |
| | | | = 85 kg × 5.7 m/s$^2$ | 1 |
| | | | = 485 N | 1 |
| | (b) | (i) | The stretching of the seatbelt increases the time it takes to halt the driver. | 1 |
| | | | This reduces the deceleration of the driver. | 1 |
| | | | So a smaller force is exerted on the driver. | 1 |
| | | (ii) | The child carries on moving when the car has stopped. | 1 |
| | | | At the speed of the car before the collision. | 1 |
| | | | Because there is no force to decelerate her. | 1 |

> **Examiner's tip** In answering this question, students often write that there is a force that propels the child forwards. This is not true (despite what it says on the television adverts). It is the lack of a force to stop her that causes the child to keep on moving.

| | | | | |
|---|---|---|---|---|
| | | (iii) | The crumpling of the car increases the stopping time. | 1 |
| | | | So the deceleration is less. | 1 |
| | | | Hence, a smaller force is needed to decelerate the occupants. | 1 |

> **Examiner's tip** Seat belts, crumple zones and air bags all increase the driver's stopping time, causing a smaller deceleration and a smaller force.

| | | | | |
|---|---|---|---|---|
| **6** | (a) | (i) | moment = force × perpendicular distance to pivot | 1 |
| | | (ii) | moment = 5 N × 8 cm = 40 N cm | 1 |

> **Examiner's tip** If you changed the distance to m, the correct answer is 0.4 N m. This shows how important it is always to ensure that you give units that are consistent with the numerical answer.

| | | | | |
|---|---|---|---|---|
| | | (iii) | force = moment ÷ distance to pivot | 1 |
| | | | = 40 N cm ÷ 2 cm = 20 N | 1 |

> **Examiner's tip** The first mark here is for transposing the moment formula.

| Question | Answer | Mark |
|---|---|---|
| (b) | **Either** increase the distance between P and B <br> **or** decrease the distance between the cork and P. | 1 |

| | | | | Mark |
|---|---|---|---|---|
| 7 | (a) | (i) | momentum = mass × velocity | 1 |
| | | | momentum = 10 000 kg × 15 m/s = 150 000 N s | 1 |
| | | (ii) | momentum = 0.1 kg × 400 m/s = 40 N s | 1 |

> **Examiner's tip** Always use kg, m and s when calculating physical quantities such as momentum and energy.

| | | | | Mark |
|---|---|---|---|---|
| | | (iii) | momentum = 500 000 kg × 300 m/s = 150 000 000 N s | 1 |
| | (b) | (i) | momentum of 30 000 kg lorry = 30 000 kg × 25 m/s | 1 |
| | | | = 750 000 N s | 1 |
| | | | momentum of 20 000 kg lorry = 20 000 kg × 15 m/s | 1 |
| | | | = 300 000 N s | 1 |
| | | (ii) | Total momentum after the collision = 1 050 000 N s | 1 |
| | | | Combined mass of lorries = 50 000 kg | 1 |
| | | | New speed = 1 050 000 N s ÷ 50 000 kg | 1 |
| | | | = 21 m/s | 1 |

> **Examiner's tip** This relies on the principle of conservation of momentum. When two objects collide, the total momentum after the collision is equal to the total momentum before the collision.

# 3 WAVES

| Question | Answer | Mark |
|---|---|---|
| 1 (a) (i) | The loudspeaker cone vibrates in and out. | 1 |
| | It does 200 complete vibrations each second. | 1 |
| (ii) | The sketches should show the air particle move to one side | 1 |
| | then back to the original position | 1 |
| | then to the other side | 1 |
| | and finally back to the original position. | 1 |
| | This is shown in the following series of diagrams: | |

| | | |
|---|---|---|
| (b) (i) | The graph should show that the amplitude of the wave is reduced. | 1 |
| | But the time to complete one cycle remains the same. | 1 |

> **Examiner's tip** These graphs can be difficult to draw precisely. Use pencil dots to mark in the positions of the top and bottom of the wave as well as any points where it crosses the time axis. Then draw the curve.

*Letts*

Q&A

| Question | Answer | Mark |
|---|---|---|

(ii)   The amplitude stays the same.                                          **1**
       One cycle is completed in half the time.                               **1**

*Examiner's tip*   This could also be shown by drawing two complete cycles in the
original time for one cycle.

(c)   Knowledge of the formula   wavelength = speed ÷ frequency               **1**
                                           = 330 m/s ÷ 200 Hz                 **1**
                                           = 1.65 m                           **1**

*Examiner's tip*   Note that the correct answer and unit gain all three marks. If the unit
is wrong or missing, the third mark is lost.

2   (a)   The completed diagrams are shown below. The marks are for:
          *Left-hand diagram*
          The wavelength in the glass is reduced.                             **1**
          The wavelength increases when the light emerges from the glass.     **1**
          *Right-hand diagram*
          The wavelength in the glass is reduced.                             **1**
          The direction of bending in the glass is correct.                   **1**
          The waves leaving the glass are parallel to those that went in.     **1**

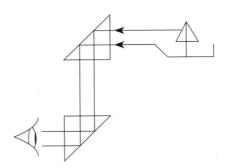

air            glass            air            air            glass            air

*Examiner's tip*   A common error when drawing the right-hand diagram is to draw the
waves in the glass parallel to the sides of the block.

(b)   One mark for each ray passing correctly through each prism.             **4**
      The correct diagram is:

| Question | Answer | Mark |
|---|---|---|
| **3** (a) | Each part of the rope vibrates or oscillates. | 1 |
| | This movement is at right angles to the direction in which the wave is travelling. | 1 |
| (b) | The amplitude is the distance from the centre position to the top of a peak or the bottom of a trough. | 1 |
| (c) | One wavelength is the length of one complete cycle, i.e. a peak and a trough. | 1 |

**Examiner's tip** The following diagram shows the amplitude (*a*) and the wavelength (λ).

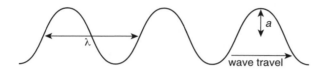

| | | |
|---|---|---|
| (d) | speed = frequency × wavelength | 1 |
| | = 1.5 Hz × 7.5 m | 1 |
| | = 11.25 m/s | 1 |

| | | |
|---|---|---|
| **4** (a) | Each arrow should be drawn at right angles to the wavefront. | |
| | A:  Pointing straight down the page. | 1 |
| | B:  Pointing straight down the page. | 1 |
| | C:  Pointing towards the bottom right-hand corner of the page. | 1 |
| (b) | The waves in the harbour are semicircular, | 1 |
| | with the same wavelength as those outside the harbour. | 1 |
| | It is called diffraction. | 1 |

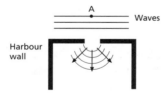

**Examiner's tip** When answering questions on diffraction, you should consider the relative sizes of the wavelength and the opening. The size of the gap in the harbour wall is not much greater than the wavelength of the water waves, so in this case there would be almost complete spreading as the waves entered the harbour. Light would not be diffracted in the same way – it would pass through as a straight beam, because the size of the gap is many times the wavelength of light.

| | | |
|---|---|---|
| (c) | Refraction. | 1 |
| (d) | The waves slow down | 1 |
| | as they enter shallow water. | 1 |

| | | |
|---|---|---|
| **5** (a) | The outer core is liquid. | 1 |

| Question | Answer | Mark |
|---|---|---|
| | As S waves are not transmitted through it. | 1 |
| (b) | The S waves do not reach the inner core, | 1 |
| | so we cannot tell whether they would pass through or not. | 1 |

> **Examiner's tip** The inner core is thought to be solid due to the increased pressure that it is under.

| Question | Answer | Mark |
|---|---|---|
| (c) | There is a change of speed **or** they are refracted. | 1 |

| | | | |
|---|---|---|---|
| 6 | (a) | When two wave crests or two wave troughs meet, they combine to give a wave of increased amplitude. | 1 |

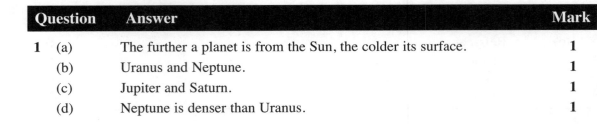

| | | | |
|---|---|---|---|
| | | | 1 |
| | | Where a wave crest meets a wave trough they combine to give a reduced amplitude. | 1 |

| | | | |
|---|---|---|---|
| | | | 1 |
| | (b) | The householder could have a very weak signal. | 1 |
| | | This would happen if the house was at a place where the waves interfered destructively. | 1 |

## 4 THE EARTH AND BEYOND

| Question | Answer | Mark |
|---|---|---|
| 1 (a) | The further a planet is from the Sun, the colder its surface. | 1 |
| (b) | Uranus and Neptune. | 1 |
| (c) | Jupiter and Saturn. | 1 |
| (d) | Neptune is denser than Uranus. | 1 |

| Question | Answer | Mark |
|---|---|---|

(e)  Jupiter.     **1**

The gravitational field strength is greatest on Jupiter, so the astronaut would be very heavy.     **1**

**Examiner's tip**   The gravitational field strength measures the size of the pull on each kilogram of material. A 60 kg person who weighs 600 N on Earth would weigh 1380 N on Jupiter.

(f)  Here is the graph:

orbital speed/km per s

radius of orbit/radius of Earth's orbit

Two marks for plotting all four points correctly, one mark for plotting two or three correctly.     **2**

One mark for drawing a smooth curve (not dot-to-dot).     **1**

(g)  Answer in the range 5.2 – 5.5 km/s.     **1**

**Examiner's tip**   This question is concerned with the scientific skills of evaluation and data handling. These are important skills that are assessed on all physics examination papers and practice of these skills should form an important part of your revision. It is important that you do not restrict your revision to learning facts, as recall of factual information only represents about 25% of the marks in physics examinations.

---

**2** (a)  It is a fusion reaction.     **1**

Hydrogen nuclei join together to form helium nuclei.     **1**

(b)  The Sun will change colour to red.     **1**

Its temperature will drop.     **1**

**Examiner's tip**   Expansion causes cooling and contraction causes heating.

(c)  (i)  Gravitational force that pulls all the particles together.     **1**

   (ii)  It will cool.     **1**

*Letts*

**Q&A**

| Question | Answer | Mark |
|----------|--------|------|
| | Its colour will change **or** its brightness will fade. | 1 |

| Question | Answer | Mark |
|----------|--------|------|
| 3 (a) | The comet speeds up as it approaches the Sun. | 1 |
| | This is caused by the increasing gravitational pull. | 1 |
| (b) | The 's' should be at the extreme right-hand side of the comet's orbit on the diagram. | 1 |

| Question | Answer | Mark |
|----------|--------|------|
| (c) (i) | Water vapour evaporates from the ice. | 1 |
| | This then reflects light from the Sun. | 1 |
| (ii) | The mass decreases when the comet is near the Sun. | 1 |
| | The mass stays the same when the comet is distant from the Sun. | 1 |
| (d) | The dust enters the Earth's atmosphere | 1 |
| | where it burns up as it falls towards the Earth. | 1 |

| Question | Answer | Mark |
|----------|--------|------|
| 4 (a) | They measure the change in frequency or wavelength of the light emitted. | 1 |
| | The greater the 'red shift', the faster the galaxy is moving. | 1 |

| Question | Answer | Mark |
|----------|--------|------|
| (b) | The further a galaxy is from the Milky Way, the faster it is moving. | 1 |
| (c) | An increasing or constant rate of expansion indicates that the Universe could go on expanding forever. | 1 |
| | A decreasing rate of expansion indicates that the Universe could reach a stable (unchanging) size | 1 |
| | or it could start to collapse. | 1 |

| Question | Answer | Mark |
|----------|--------|------|
| 5 (a) | It increases/becomes greater. | 1 |
| (b) (i) | 24 hours/one day. | 1 |

| Question | Answer | | Mark |
|---|---|---|---|
| (ii) | Answer in range 35 to 36 million metres. | | 1 |
| (c) | *One mark each for any two points from:*<br>It can monitor changing weather conditions.<br>It can view different parts of the Earth's surface.<br>It gives better resolution OR greater accuracy.<br>It scans the whole of the Earth several times a day. | | 2 |

## 5 ENERGY RESOURCES AND ENERGY TRANSFER

| Question | Answer | | Mark |
|---|---|---|---|
| 1 (a) | A man pushing a supermarket trolley. | ✓ | 1 |
| | A girl pedalling a bicycle. | ✓ | 1 |
| | A shelf supporting some books. | | 1 |
| | A gas flame heating some water. | ✓ | 1 |
| | The weight of a building pushing down on the ground. | | 1 |
| | Water evaporating from the sea. | ✓ | 1 |
| | The upward push of the sea on a floating ship. | | 1 |
| | The upward push on a rising hot-air balloon. | ✓ | 1 |
| (b) | 19 J | | 1 |
| | of thermal energy (heat). | | 1 |

**Examiner's tip** This is an example of the principle of conservation of energy, which states that energy cannot be created or destroyed; it can only change from one form into others. This means that the total energy going into a device must equal the total energy that comes out.

| | | | |
|---|---|---|---|
| 2 (a) | (i) Any four from: gas, oil, coal, tar, uranium, geothermal (1 mark each). | | 4 |
| | (ii) Any four from wind, wave, hydroelectric, tides, timber, food (1 mark each). | | 4 |

**Examiner's tip** Although vegetation such as timber is renewable, coal is not. This is because the timescale over which coal is formed from rotting vegetation is millions of years.

| | | | |
|---|---|---|---|
| | (iii) Hydroelectric power stores energy from the Sun as gravitational potential energy of water. | | 1 |
| | (iv) Any two from: food, timber, coal, oil, gas, tar (1 mark each). | | 2 |
| (b) | (i) Black is the best absorber of radiant energy. | | 1 |
| | (ii) Copper is a better conductor of thermal energy. | | 1 |
| | Copper does not corrode. | | 1 |
| | (iii) The box acts like a greenhouse. | | 1 |
| | It reduces the amount of energy lost by radiation (heat). | | 1 |

| Question | Answer | Mark |
|---|---|---|

| (iv) | Water is heated in the pipes and rises. | 1 |
| | This happens because it is less dense than the colder water. | 1 |
| | Cold, denser water from the bottom of the tank moves down to replace it. | 1 |

| 3 (a) | Efficiency = 3 MW ÷ 9 MW | 1 |
| | = 0.33 | 1 |

| (b) | Wind turbines have low running costs. | 1 |
| | They do not use fossil reserves. | 1 |
| | They do not cause atmospheric pollution. | 1 |
| (c) | Wind turbines occupy a lot of room. | 1 |
| | They are noisy/do not work if there is no wind. | 1 |

| 4 (a) | Air at the top of the refrigerator is cooled. | 1 |
| | This cold air falls | 1 |
| | and pushes the warmer air up. | 1 |

| (b) | The wire shelves allow the air to circulate in the refrigerator. | 1 |
| (c) | Convection currents cannot occur because the gases are trapped in the expanded polystyrene. | 1 |
| | Radiant energy is reflected by the aluminium foil. | 1 |

| (d) | Evaporation of a liquid requires energy. | 1 |
| | This is taken from the surroundings, causing them to cool. | 1 |

| 5 (a) (i) | change in gpe $= mg\Delta h$ | 1 |
| | $= 3100\,\text{kg} \times 10\,\text{N/kg} \times 72\,\text{m}$ | 1 |
| | $= 2\,232\,000\,\text{J}$ | 1 |

| Question | Answer | Mark |
|---|---|---|
| (ii) | time = energy transfer ÷ power | 1 |
| | = 2 232 000 J ÷ 50 000 W | 1 |
| | = 44.6 s | 1 |
| (iii) | Some power is needed to work against resistive forces. | 1 |
| | The power remaining to lift the carriages is less than 50 kW. | 1 |
| (b) (i) | Gravitational potential energy is transferred to kinetic energy. | 1 |
| (ii) | Loss of gpe between B and C = 3100 kg × 10 N/kg × 65.5 m | |
| | = 2 030 500 J | 1 |
| | gain in ke, $\frac{1}{2}mv^2$ = 2 030 500 J | 1 |
| | $v^2$ = 2 030 500 J ÷ ($\frac{1}{2}$ × 3100 kg) = 1310 (m/s)$^2$ | 1 |
| | so $v$ = 36.2 m/s | 1 |

| Question | Answer | Mark |
|---|---|---|
| (iii) | The carriage loses some energy to heat due to resistive forces, so it would not be able to reach the height of B. | 1 |
| | The carriage needs to have some kinetic energy remaining at D, otherwise it would stop. | 1 |
| 6 | Energy absorbed = mass × shc × temperature rise | 1 |
| | = 6.3 kg × 4200 J kg$^{-1}$°C$^{-1}$ × 90°C | 1 |
| | = 2.38 MJ or 2.38 × 10$^6$ J | 1 |

# 6 ATOMIC AND MOLECULAR PHYSICS

| Question | Answer | Mark |
|---|---|---|
| 1 (a) | Gamma | 1 |
| | Alpha | 1 |
| | Beta | 1 |
| (b) (i) | The paper became thinner. | 1 |
| | The person can tell this because of the increase in radiation penetrating the paper. | 1 |

| Question | Answer | Mark |
|---|---|---|
| (ii) | $^{90}$Sr | 1 |
| (iii) | The source should emit beta radiation. | 1 |
| | Alpha would not penetrate and gamma would not be affected by the | |

| Question | | Answer | Mark |
|---|---|---|---|
| | | change in thickness of the paper. | 1 |
| | | It should have a long half-life, | 1 |
| | | so that it does not need frequent recalibration because of the decrease in activity due to its decay. | 1 |
| | (c) | Any four points from the following (1 mark each): | |
| | | avoid direct handling; | |
| | | wear protective clothing; | |
| | | store sources in lead containers; | |
| | | people who work with radioactive substances should have their 'dose' continually monitored; | |
| | | never point a source towards a body; | |
| | | no eating or drinking where radioactive sources are being used. | 4 |
| 2 | (a) | Gamma radiation penetrates body tissue. | 1 |
| | | Very little is absorbed to damage the patient. | 1 |
| | (b) | Both would be absorbed by the body tissue. | 1 |
| | | They would cause ionisation and cell damage. | 1 |
| | | They could also cause gene mutations. | 1 |
| | (c) (i) | Half-life is the time interval | 1 |
| | | that it takes for the rate of decay (or the number of undecayed nuclei) to halve. | 1 |

**Examiner's tip**   It is a common misconception that a radioactive source becomes inactive after two half-lives. This is not true, in fact the activity is then a quarter of the original activity.

| | (ii) | It remains active long enough to permeate the body and for photographs to be taken. | 1 |
|---|---|---|---|
| | | But it is short enough so that the concentration of radioactive material in the patient's body quickly falls to a very low level. | 1 |
| 3 | (a) | Thick cast iron walls are needed because of the large pressure of the gas inside the cylinder. | 1 |
| | (b) | $PV = $ constant | 1 |
| | | $2.4 \times 10^7 \text{ Pa} \times 300 \text{ cm}^3 = 1.01 \times 10^5 \text{ Pa} \times V$ | 1 |
| | | $V = \dfrac{2.4 \times 10^7 \times 300 \text{ cm}^3}{1.01 \times 10^5} = 71\,287 \text{ cm}^3$ | 1 |
| | (c) | $70\,987 \text{ cm}^3$ | 1 |

**Examiner's tip**   Gas emerges from the cylinder until the pressure inside the cylinder is equal to atmospheric pressure; 300 cm³ of gas remain inside the cylinder.

| 4 | (a) | The gas particles are in constant motion. | 1 |
|---|---|---|---|
| | | Pressure is caused by collisions with the walls of the container. | 1 |

| Question | Answer | Mark |
|---|---|---|

(b) $P_1V_1 = P_2V_2$
$1 \times 10^7 \, \text{N/m}^2 \times 0.1 \, \text{m}^3$ (1 mark) $= 1.2 \times 10^5 \, \text{N/m}^2 \times V_2$ (1 mark)    **2**
volume $= 8.3 \, \text{m}^3$    **1**

(c) $8.3 \, \text{m}^3 \div 1 \times 10^{-2}$
$= 830 \text{ OR } 833 \, \text{m}^3$    **2**

---

**5** (a) The motion of the smoke particle is random or disordered in direction.    **1**
It moves varying distances between changing course.    **1**

(b) The smoke particle is being hit by things which cannot be seen under a microscope.    **1**
Therefore, the things must be very small.    **1**
Given the difference in size, they must be moving very rapidly to make the smoke particle move.    **1**
They must also be moving in all directions, as there is no pattern to the movement of the smoke particle.    **1**

---

# 7 MOCK EXAMINATION PAPER

| Question | Answer | Mark |
|---|---|---|

**1** (a) The completed graph is shown on the right. Allow two marks for plotting all the points correctly (one mark if one or two errors are made).    **2**
One mark for drawing the best straight line through the first four points, becoming a curve between the last two points.    **1**

(b) 11.0 cm    **1**

(c) 3.5 cm    **1**

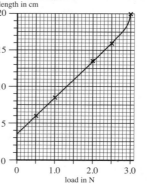

| Question | Answer | Mark |
|---|---|---|

The line needs to be drawn back (as shown) to where it crosses the y-axis to find the length when the load is zero.

(d)    Up to 2.5 N.      1

For this range of forces the graph is a straight line.    1

---

**2**   (a)    time = distance ÷ speed      1

= 270 miles ÷ 60 mph    1

= 4.5 hours    1

Award full marks for the correct answer and unit, but no marks are available if you made an error in rearranging the speed equation.

(b)    kinetic energy = $\frac{1}{2}$ mv$^2$      1

= $\frac{1}{2}$ × 900 kg × (30 m/s)$^2$    1

= 405 000 J    1

A common error in calculating kinetic energy is to work out $(\frac{1}{2} mv)^2$, squaring the whole of the expression instead of just the speed. To work out kinetic energy using your calculator you should first key in the speed, then square it before multiplying by half the mass.

(c)    time = energy transfer ÷ power      1

= 405 000 J ÷ 67 500 W    1

= 6 s    1

(d)    distance travelled = average speed × time      1

= 15 m/s × 6 s    1

= 90 m    1

Some candidates find the concept of average speed difficult. If a car travelling at 30 m/s brakes uniformly to a halt (0 m/s), then the average speed during braking is the speed half way through, ie 15 m/s.

(e)    Travelling at 30 m/s, the car now has more kinetic energy.    1

The car travels further while braking since it takes longer to remove this energy.    1

---

**3**   (a)    The light strikes the edges at an angle that is greater than the critical angle.   1

So it is all reflected internally.    1

(b)    An endoscope consisting of two bundles of fibres is inserted into the patient, e.g. through the mouth.    1

Light is passed down one bundle of fibres.    1

Reflected light passes up the other bundle of fibres to a television camera, enabling a view of the interior of the patient on a television screen.    1

The advantage of an endoscope is that it enables light to be transmitted round corners, allowing diagnosis and microsurgery to be performed without making openings in the patient's flesh.

| Question | Answer | Mark |
|---|---|---|
| **4** (a) | Your diagram should show semicircular waves centred at the centre of the gap. <br> With the wavelength unchanged. | 1 <br> 1 |

| | | |
|---|---|---|
| (b) | Diffraction. | 1 |
| (c) | Light passes through as a straight beam with no visible spreading. <br> Because the size of the gap is very many times the wavelength of light. | 1 <br> 1 |
| **5** (a) | Moons orbit the planets. <br> Planets orbit the Sun. | 1 <br> 1 |
| (b) | Planets all orbit in the same plane OR a thin disc. <br> All the planets orbit in the same direction. <br> The orbits of planets are almost circular. <br> Comets can orbit in any plane. <br> Comets can orbit in any direction. <br> Comet orbits can be highly elliptical. <br> One mark each for any four points. | 4 |
| (c) | Between Mars (1 mark) and Jupiter (1 mark) <br> Allow both marks if you answered 'between the inner and the outer planets'. | 2 |
| (d) | A star contracts due to the attractive gravitational forces. <br> As it contracts, it heats and glows very brightly. <br> The explosion is due to the intense heating OR very high temperature. | 1 <br> 1 <br> 1 |
| (e) | Parts of the dust cloud contract due to the attractive gravitational forces. <br> This causes heating. <br> A star is formed when the temperature is high enough for fusion reactions to take place. | 1 <br> 1 <br> 1 |
| (f) | The fusion reactions. <br> Energy is released when light nuclei fuse together to form more massive ones. | 1 <br> 1 |
| (g) | It will expand and cool <br> forming a red giant. <br> It will then contract into a white dwarf. | 1 <br> 1 <br> 1 |
| **6** (a) | Energy is needed to evaporate the coolant. <br> This energy is taken from its surroundings. | 1 <br> 1 |
| (b | Black is a good emitter <br> of infra-red radiation. | 1 <br> 1 |

| Question | Answer | Mark |
|---|---|---|
| (c) | Air warmed by the pipes rises. | 1 |
| | It is replaced by colder air from below. | 1 |
| | This movement of air forms a convection current. | 1 |
| (d) | The gap is necessary to allow free movement of air. | 1 |
| | A smaller gap would reduce the airflow and less heat would be removed. | 1 |
| | Consequently the inside of the refrigerator would be too warm. | 1 |

| Question | Answer | Mark |
|---|---|---|
| 7 (a) (i) | B | 1 |
| (ii) | C | 1 |
| (iii) | A | 1 |
| (b) | The half-life is the average time | 1 |
| | taken for half the undecayed nuclei in a sample to decay. | 1 |

**Examiner's tip**  Since radioactive decay is a random process, it is important to stress the average time.

| | | |
|---|---|---|
| (c) (i) | Geiger-Müller tube and counter. | 1 |
| (ii) | 260 counts/s | 1 |
| | 130 counts/s | 1 |

**Examiner's tip**  A common error is to state that all the material has decayed after two half-lives. This is not the case; after two half-lives the activity has dropped to $0.5 \times 0.5 = 0.25$ of the original activity.

| | | |
|---|---|---|
| (iii) | Because of the random nature of radioactive decay. | 1 |
| | The actual activity can vary from that predicted. | 1 |

| | | |
|---|---|---|
| 8 (a) | current = voltage ÷ resistance | 1 |
| | $= 6\ V \div 240\ \Omega$ | 1 |
| | $= 0.025\ A$ | 1 |
| (b) | When a current passes in it the coil has a magnetic field. | 1 |
| | This magnetises the iron core. | 1 |
| | The L-shaped armature is pulled to the end of the core. | 1 |
| | This presses the switch contacts together. | 1 |

**Examiner's tip**  The coil has a very weak magnetic field, but it readily magnetises the iron which has a strong magnetic field.

| | | |
|---|---|---|
| (c) | *One mark each for any two points from:* | |
| | It allows a large current to be switched by a small one. | |
| | A high voltage circuit can be switched using a low voltage. | |
| | Thin wires can be used when the switch is not close to the | |
| | device being switched. | 1 |

### Marking your test

Use the marking scheme to mark your test. If you are not sure about any of your answers, ask your teacher. When you have a mark for the test out of 75 marks, you can use this table to estimate your likely grade. Remember, however, that this is just one test and so you cannot be sure you will get this grade every time. It will give you an indication of your level of achievement.

| Mark in the test | Grade |
|---|---|
| Over 60 | A* |
| 52–60 | A |
| 45–51 | B |
| 38–44 | C |
| 25–37 | D |
| Less than 25 | Ungraded |